# Roads
# to Everywhere

REVISED EDITION

- DAVID H. RUSSELL
- DORIS GATES
- CONSTANCE M. McCULLOUGH

GINN AND COMPANY | BOSTON · NEW YORK · CHICAGO · ATLANTA
DALLAS · PALO ALTO · TORONTO

# Acknowledgments

Grateful acknowledgment is made to the following authors and publishers for permission to use and adapt copyrighted materials:

Thomas Y. Crowell Company, for "The Chopper," adapted from *Helicopters: How They Work*, by John Lewellen, copyright, 1954, by John Lewellen, reprinted by permission of the publishers, Thomas Y. Crowell Company, New York.

Doubleday & Company, Inc., for "Seal Lullaby," from *The Jungle Book*, by Rudyard Kipling, reprinted by permission of Mrs. George Bambridge and Doubleday & Company, Inc.; and for "If Only," from *Gay Go Up*, by Rose Fyleman, copyright, 1929, 1930, by Doubleday & Company, Inc., reprinted by permission of the publisher, Doubleday & Company, Inc.

E. P. Dutton & Co., Inc., for "The Secret Cave," adapted from the book *The Secret Cave*, by Florence McClurg Everson and Howard Everson, copyright, 1930, by E. P. Dutton & Co., Inc., renewal, 1958, by Florence McClurg Everson and Howard Everson; for "Bruce and the Spider," adapted from the book *Favorite Tales of Long Ago*, by James Baldwin, copyright, 1955, by The American Book Company; for "The Snowshoe Rabbit Escapes," adapted from the book *Trapped by the Mountain Storm*, by Aileen Fisher, copyright, 1950, by Aileen Fisher; and for "Timbuctoo," from *Around and About*, by Marchette Chute, copyright, 1932, by Marchette Chute. All reprinted by permission of the publishers, E. P. Dutton & Co., Inc.

Alfred A. Knopf, Inc., for "Old Tom," adapted from *Up Hill and Down*, by Elizabeth Coatsworth, copyright, 1947, by Elizabeth Coatsworth; for "Freddy, the Detective," adapted from *Freddy Goes Camping*, by Walter R. Brooks, copyright, 1948, by Walter R. Brooks; and for "The Polar Bear," reprinted from *Cautionary Verses*, by Hilaire Belloc, published in 1941 by Alfred A. Knopf, Inc. All by permission of the publisher, Alfred A. Knopf, Inc.

The Macmillan Company, for "Adventure at the Falls," adapted from *The Peddler's Cart*, by Elizabeth Coatsworth, copyright, 1956; and for "Wings to the North," adapted from *Across Canada*, by Clare Bice, copyright, 1949; both by permission of the publisher, The Macmillan Company.

McGraw-Hill Book Company, Inc., for "When You Go to the Zoo," from *When You Go to the Zoo*, by Glenn O. Blough and Marjorie H. Campbell, published by Whittlesey House, copyright ©, 1955, by Glenn O. Blough and Marjorie Haines Campbell, with permission of McGraw-Hill Book Company, Inc.

Prentice-Hall, Inc., for "To the Moon and Back," adapted with permission of the publishers from *The Prentice-Hall Book About Space Travel*, by William F. Temple, copyright ©, 1954, by William F. Temple.

Rinehart & Company, Inc., for "The Back of the Bus," adapted from *The Four-Story Mistake*, by Elizabeth Enright, copyright, 1942, by Elizabeth Enright Gillham, with the permission of Rinehart & Company, Inc., Publishers.

G. Schirmer, Inc., for "The Fisherman," translated by Anne Higginson Spicer, reprinted from *The Botsford Collection of Folk Songs*, used by permission of G. Schirmer, Inc., copyright, 1929, 1933, by G. Schirmer, Inc.

Charles Scribner's Sons, for "The Family Who Had Never Had an Automobile," adapted from *Time Was*, by Hildegard Woodward, copyright, 1941, by Charles Scribner's Sons; for "Ducks' Ditty," reprinted from *The Wind in the Willows*, by Kenneth Grahame, copyright, 1908, by Charles Scribner's Sons; and for "Windy Nights," from *A Child's Garden of Verses*, by Robert Louis Stevenson; all by permission of the publisher.

2

Frederick Muller, Ltd., London, for "To the Moon and Back," adapted from *The Prentice-Hall Book About Space Travel*, by William F. Temple.

The National Bank & Trust Company of Fairfield County, Stamford, Connecticut, for permission to reprint "Dogs and Weather," by Winifred Welles, from *Skipping Along Alone*, published by The Macmillan Company.

The New York Sun, Inc., for "Cockpit in the Clouds," by Dick Dorrance.

Oxford University Press, London, for "The Five Chinese Brothers," adapted from *The Five Chinese Brothers*, by Claire Huchet Bishop, copyrighted, 1938, by Claire Huchet Bishop and Kurt Wiese.

The Society of Authors, London, as the Literary Representative of the Estate of the late Rose Fyleman, for "If Only," from *Gay Go Up*, by Rose Fyleman; and as representative of the Literary Trustees of Walter de la Mare, for his poem "Someone."

Story Parade, Inc., for "John Hudson's Surprise," adapted from *The Flaming River*, by Mosser Mauger, copyright, 1941, by Story Parade, Inc., reprinted by permission of Story Parade, Inc.

Dorothy Brown Thompson, for "Maps."

Nancy Byrd Turner, for "Lincoln," from *Child Life Magazine*, copyright, 1929, by Rand McNally & Company, and for "Washington," from *Child Life Magazine*, copyright, 1930, by Rand McNally & Company.

The Viking Press, for "Magic Money," adapted from *Magic Money*, by Ann Nolan Clark, copyright, 1950, by Ann Nolan Clark and Leo Politi, reprinted by permission of The Viking Press, Inc., New York; for "Just Enough," adapted from *Sarah's Idea*, by Doris Gates, copyright, 1938, by Doris Gates and Marjorie Torrey, reprinted by permission of The Viking Press, Inc.; for "Mister Penny," adapted from *Mister Penny*, by Marie Hall Ets, copyright, 1935, by Marie Hall Ets, by permission of The Viking Press, Inc.; and for "Sur-Dah, the Lion," adapted from *Lions on the Hunt*, by Theodore J. Waldeck, copyright, 1942, by The Viking Press, Inc., and reprinted with their permission.

Woodfield and Stanley, Ltd., for "Mister Penny," adapted from *Mister Penny*, by Marie Hall Ets.

---

# Contents

## Adventure Waits

## Old Favorites

## Wheels and Wings

## They Worked to Win

## Here Come the Animals

## Fun and Nonsense

6

# To the Rescue

# Neighbors Round the World

# Adventure Waits

Here's an adventure!   What awaits
Beyond these closed, mysterious gates?
Whom shall I meet, where shall I go?
Beyond the lovely land I know?
Above the sky, across the sea?
What shall I learn and feel and be?
Open, strange doors, to good or ill!
I hold my breath a moment still
Before the magic of your look.
What will you do to me, O book?

9

# Benjie and the Pilot

## The Mail Plane

Benjie came slowly from the barn. He stopped to watch the silver wings of the mail plane crossing the sky. Then he jerked a white cloth from his pocket and waved it.

Benjie thought how lucky he was. The mail plane crossed the sky above his house every day. Carrying mail by plane was new in 1925.

"Supper! Supper!" his sister Ella called, running toward Benjie. "Did you see the plane, Benjie? Do you think the pilot saw you?"

"Yes, he dipped a wing," said Benjie. Then he followed Ella into the house.

"The plane was late tonight," his father said as the family sat down to supper.

"I'd like to fly the mail," Benjie said dreamily.

"You fly a plane!" His father looked surprised. "Why, you are even afraid to ride old Nellie!"

Benjie looked very unhappy. He was ashamed of this fear which he could not overcome.

It had started one far-off day when Benjie was a small boy. To his delight, he was lifted to the gentle horse's back. Then Nellie shook herself hard. Poor Benjie would have slipped off if his father had not caught him. Delight changed to fear. Benjie was frightened, badly frightened. From that day he had been afraid of horses, and a reminder of this old fear stung with the sharpness of a bee's sting.

11

"Could I learn to fly?" he'd ask himself each day as he watched the sky for the mail plane. His father's voice always answered him, "Why, you are even afraid to ride old Nellie!"

Benjie was again reminded of his old fear one cold afternoon a few weeks later. He stood beside the driveway, swinging his arms to keep warm. His father was just getting into the car.

"I wish you could come along, Benjie," Ella said, peeping out through the car curtains.

"Somebody has to stay and finish the work," said Benjie. "It's my turn tonight."

"Your supper is on the stove, ready for you," his mother said. "Be careful."

"The church supper may make us late getting home," his father warned him before driving off.

By the time Benjie was through with his work, it was dark. He looked up at the sky, now full of flying snow. Everything was still. The animals had quieted down for the night. Slowly he crossed the barnyard and went into the kitchen to have his supper.

An hour later Benjie lighted a lantern and carried it outside. His ears were listening in the stillness for the roar of a motor.

12

In a moment he heard something high overhead. It was not a steady roar that died away into the darkness. It was the broken throb of an engine which was not running smoothly. A plane was circling above him.

"He wants to land!" Benjie said to himself.

Suddenly he turned and ran into the barn. There he picked up an armful of hay and started for the pasture. The lantern swayed from side to side as he ran.

For a second a bright light flashed in front of him. It was dropping from the sky. Then all was black again. The pilot had dropped a flare, but what had happened to it? Flares were supposed to drop slowly and light the pilot's way to the ground.

When Benjie reached the fence, he threw the hay over and climbed after it. Quickly he opened the lantern and pushed in a large handful of hay.

It took only a second to light the handful and throw it into the pile of hay. Flames shot up from the snow-covered ground, and the empty pasture showed clearly in the bright light from the burning hay. Then the fire died down as quickly as it had flared up.

Overhead the unsteady throbbing of the motor sounded closer and closer. Benjie began to swing the lighted lantern back and forth. With a roar and a swish of cold air the plane passed him and stopped.

Benjie ran toward it, holding his lantern high.

14

"Good boy!" the pilot said, climbing out. "You saved me and my plane. I lost my flare, but that fire was enough to shine me down. Your lantern helped too."

The pilot began to take mailbags out of the plane. "Have you a telephone?" he asked.

"No," said Benjie.

"Got a car? I have to get this mail into town for the nine o'clock train."

"We have a horse," Benjie said helpfully. "It's not very far into town from here. A horse could make it in time."

"Good!" said the pilot. "A horse will do! How old are you?"

"Twelve," Benjie answered.

"Do you think you could carry the mail to town on horseback?" the pilot asked.

Benjie had a sick feeling. His heart seemed to drop down into his boots. He had thought that the pilot would ride the horse.

"I'd ride in myself," the pilot said as if he knew what Benjie was thinking. "But I must get to work on the plane's engine. It's not running smoothly. I'll have to make some repairs and keep the engine warmed up, or it won't start in the morning. This biting cold makes engines hard to start."

"Ye-es, sir," said Benjie. He wondered if he sounded as scared as he felt.

Benjie led the way to the barn and held the lantern while the pilot saddled Nellie and fastened on the mailbags.

To Benjie, old Nellie had never looked so big before. She seemed as high up as a mountain. He wondered how he would ever climb onto her back.

The next minute the pilot had lifted him up, swinging him into the saddle. He picked up the reins, and Nellie walked quietly out of the barn. They were on their way to town.

16

## A Race with Time

Benjie tried to remember everything his father
had told him about riding. "Get the feel of the
horse and give in to it. A good horse will make
his own way if you let him."

Well, Nellie was a good horse. That much
Benjie knew.

Soon he loosened his hold on the saddle and
held the reins less tightly. Snow was blowing
into Nellie's eyes, but she
didn't seem one bit afraid.
She knew the way to town.

Suddenly far off through
the still air came the sound
of a whistle. That was the
nine o'clock train! Benjie
forgot all about himself and
his fear. He remembered
only that he had to get the
mail to the station on time.

"Get up!" he called out
to Nellie and gave her a
sharp slap.

Surprised by the slap, the old horse broke into a gallop. For a second Benjie thought surely he would go flying over Nellie's head. Then his body began to swing in time with the horse's gallop. He was riding, really riding! He shouted with joy.

Ahead of them the lights of the town were shining. The old horse slowed down as she reached the station. Again came the whistle. The train was coming round the bend. Benjie pulled on the reins, and Nellie stopped.

"There's mail here for that train!" Benjie called out, and the station master came running.

A great load seemed to fall from Benjie's shoulders as he handed over the mailbags. He watched the station master put them on the train. Then he shivered in the cold December air.

18

"Come into the station and get warm, boy," said the station master. "I'll take care of your horse."

After Nellie had rested, boy and horse were on the road again. They were headed toward home. High in the black sky the moon edged its way out from behind a cloud. It had stopped snowing.

Benjie patted Nellie's neck. How could he have ever been scared of this gentle old horse? He would never again be afraid to ride her.

When Benjie rode into the barnyard, his father was out there watching for him. "Good work, son," he said. Then he helped Benjie slide off the horse and led her into the barn.

His mother and Ella looked up at Benjie when he walked into the kitchen. They were proud of him, but they acted as if Benjie rode Nellie every day. That pleased him. He didn't want the pilot to know that he was ever afraid to ride Nellie.

"Mr. Harper told us where you were," Benjie's mother said. She turned toward the pilot, who was having supper in the kitchen.

"I got there in time, Mr. Harper," Benjie said. "The train was just coming in."

"I knew you'd make it," said the pilot.

Before the family went to bed, Benjie and his father brought in more wood for the stove. The pilot was going to spend the night sleeping in a big chair. He had to start the plane's motor from time to time. He wanted to keep it warmed up for an early morning take-off.

The next morning, as soon as it was daylight, Benjie looked out of his window. He could just make out the pilot at work on his plane. Dressing quickly, Benjie hurried out to the pasture.

"How's the plane this morning, Mr. Harper?" he called over the steady roar of the motor.

"Fine!" said the pilot. "How are you?" He cut the motor and turned to look down at the boy beside him. "You were scared last night when you rode to town, weren't you?"

Benjie kicked at the soft snow. "Yes," he said. "I was scared! I thought I couldn't make it."

"I've been scared at times," the pilot said. "I have thought I couldn't make it sometimes up there in the sky alone. I guess everyone gets scared at times. The important thing is to make it, anyway." He put his hand on the boy's shoulder. "I'd like to teach you to fly someday, Benjie. You'd make a good pilot."

20

He got into the plane and put on his heavy gloves and his sunglasses. "You be watching about noon. I'll be headed back with the mail."

"You won't forget to teach me to fly?" Benjie had to shout the words, for the pilot had started up the motor again. Its roar filled the pasture.

"I won't forget. It's a promise," the pilot shouted back.

The plane circled the field, its motor purring. Then it began to lift. Benjie watched the silver wings crossing the sky. Quickly he jerked the white cloth out of his pocket and waved it.

*Jane W. Krows*

# The Secret Cave

## *A Young Explorer*

When Sammy Andy was ten years old, his uncle gave him a flashlight. The present made Sammy happy because for a long time he had wanted to do some exploring. Everyone knows that you can't do much exploring without a flashlight, not in a cave anyway!

Sammy had found a cave. It was on the farm where he lived with his grandfather and grandmother. He and Rex, the farm dog, had been following the brook one day. They had just reached the place where the brook ran out of a hillside.

There Rex had started to sniff under some rocks, and Sammy had become interested. He had moved away some of the rocks and found a tiny opening. By digging away a few more rocks, he had been able to wiggle through. Rex had wiggled into the cave right behind him.

They had stood very close together in the cold darkness, not making a sound. It wasn't that Sammy was really afraid, just surprised. He had felt, all of a sudden, very glad to have Rex along. After a few minutes he and Rex had wiggled back into the sunshine.

From that day the wish to explore the cave had filled Sammy's thoughts. He knew it would be a foolish thing to do without a flashlight. So he had told the family that he would like to have one.

"Why in the world do you want a flashlight?" his grandmother had asked.

There the matter had stopped. The cave was his secret, and he didn't want to talk about it. A secret cave was fun to think about.

Now it was a Saturday morning a year later, and Sammy had his flashlight. Right after breakfast he packed a lunch and set out. Rex was waiting for him, and they went off together. After a while they came to the hillside and the secret cave.

Sammy moved the stones away from the opening, and he and Rex wiggled in. As soon as they reached the other side, Sammy pressed the button of his flashlight. It shone on a large room with wet, shiny walls.

24

Out of a deep crack in the back wall ran a little brook. It ran across the cave and under the front wall. Sammy knew it was the same brook he had followed to the cave. He walked toward it slowly, his flashlight shining on the deep crack.

There must be another cave on the other side of the wall, he thought. A brook couldn't just come out of nowhere. If he could dig under the wall, he might be able to crawl through there.

Putting down the flashlight very gently, Sammy went to work. It was easy digging along the smooth, sandy banks of the brook.

He didn't have much luck in making the opening larger. As fast as he dug away the sand, the water spread out and filled in the opening. At last he had to give it up. With his flashlight he explored the back wall to find another crack.

# Inside the Cave

Just then there was a loud crash. What was that noise? Sammy turned his light toward the sound to see what had made it.

He had dug away sand on which the rocks of the back wall were resting. As the brook had washed away the sand, the rocks had settled down. One large rock near the roof had crashed to the floor. A hole like a window was left in the wall.

Sammy climbed up and held his flashlight to the hole. What a sight met his eyes!

Sparkling in the light were walls like pink coral and strange, rocky posts. The cave seemed to stretch for miles and miles into darkness. Long pieces of sparkling pink stone were hanging from the top of the cave, and it all looked like fairyland.

Now Sammy felt just like an explorer. He was sure that no other eyes but his had ever looked upon this sight.

Slowly he began crawling through the opening. It wasn't easy with his flashlight in one hand and his lunch in the other, but he got there at last. Rex did not follow him into this pink fairyland.

"Here, Rex," called Sammy. "Come on, old boy." Rex did not come. He may have been cold or afraid of the darkness.

Sammy walked ahead slowly, holding the flashlight out in front of him. The bottom of the cave was hard rock. Every footstep he took made a loud, hollow sound. At his feet the little brook went smoothly and quietly along.

Suddenly he saw something that stopped him right in his tracks. His heart began to beat very fast. The flashlight shook a little in his hand. There in the sand beside the brook were two footprints! They were large footprints and had been made by a man.

Just when they had been pressed into the sand he could not tell. One thing was sure, he was not the first person to look upon this place. Someone had been here before him. That person might be hiding in the cave now!

Sammy was scared. He forgot all about wanting to be an explorer. He just wanted to get out of the cave quickly.

Turning, he ran as fast as he could back along the way he had come. He raced over the wet rocks, with the flashlight swinging wildly. Then he tripped and fell. The flashlight slipped out of his hand and broke as it crashed to the cave floor. The next second Sammy was in darkness.

"Now what shall I do?" Sammy asked himself. It was darker than the inside of a pocket.

Sammy knew it would be foolish to try to find his way out of the cave. He wasn't even sure which way he should take. He felt trapped.

There was only one thing to do. He must settle down and stay right in this spot until he was rescued, whenever that might be! It wasn't a very happy thought. If Sammy hadn't been a real explorer, he might have started to cry.

Anyway, a thought had come to make him feel better. Rex knew where he was. There was a chance that Rex would remember the cave and bring someone back with him before too long!

## Rescue

Rex did remember. When it got toward dinner time, no hungry boy came banging into the kitchen. So Grandmother began to hunt for Sammy.

Rex followed her about. He seemed to be trying to tell her something. He even pulled at the edge of her apron when she asked, "Where's Sammy?"

Grandmother began to worry. She went to look for Grandfather.

29

Grandfather called John, who helped on the farm. The two of them set out to hunt for Sammy. Rex trotted ahead, leading them straight to the place where the brook ran out of the hillside.

"Well, well," Grandfather said, "I wonder why he brought us here. Sammy couldn't have gone into the hillside!"

Rex began sniffing at the hole where he and Sammy had wiggled into the cave.

Grandfather got down on his knees and began throwing rocks to one side. Soon he had made a big enough opening so that he could crawl through. Then he, too, was standing in Sammy's secret cave.

"Sammy!" called Grandfather, "Sam-my!"

From far away came an answering shout, "Here, Grandfather! I'm in here."

30

"Stay—right—where—you—are!" Grandfather shouted the words very slowly. He wanted the echo of each word to end before the next word came along. "I'm going—to get—a lantern."

"All right," Sammy called back, and an echo answered, "All right."

Soon he saw the lighted lantern bobbing toward him, and there were Grandfather and John and Rex. Sammy was so glad to see them that he didn't even mind the scolding he got.

"Why didn't you tell us where you were going?" asked Grandfather.

"It was a secret," Sammy said, "but I'll never do it again. It's no fun being lost in the dark, even if you are an explorer."

"A good explorer always leaves word about where he's going," scolded Grandfather. "He never, never goes digging under rocks without finding out if it's safe. What if some of those big rocks had fallen on top of you!"

When Sammy thought about that, his knees felt weak. "I'll remember," he promised. Then he told about the footprints.

"They must have been made in early times by cave men," said his grandfather. "Let's do a bit of exploring and see."

So the three of them walked on for about half a mile. Grandfather led the way with the lantern. Then they really did have a surprise!

On the floor were stones that had been made into hammers and other tools. Here and there were arrowheads and stone dishes and bowls. In a jar were some bright-colored beads.

"These things were made by men in very, very early days," said Grandfather. "They must have lived and worked here long before white men came to this country. Tomorrow we'll call Mr. Black at the museum and tell him about the cave. I'm sure he'll want to have these things for the museum."

That made Sammy feel like a real explorer all right. After all, wasn't he really one? He had found the cave, and so these old treasures were brought to light. Now they would be in the museum for everyone to see.

*Florence and Howard Everson*

# The Back of the Bus

## Two-Wheelers

Randy Melendy was standing at the west window of the tower room. From there she could see far down the road that ran past the funny old house.

This was the day when their good friend Mrs. Oliphant was to arrive in the old station wagon.

Mrs. Oliphant was like part of the family to the four motherless children. Cuffy, the housekeeper, was kind and motherly, but it was Mrs. Oliphant who always brought adventure with her when she came for a visit.

Randy stayed at the window most of the afternoon. So she was the first to see the station wagon turn into the driveway.

33

"Here she comes!" shouted Randy, racing down the stairs to the front hall.

Shouts of joy answered her from all over the house. Father burst out of his room. Cuffy burst out of the kitchen. The front door was thrown open, and left that way. The old station wagon grumbled to a stop. Mrs. Oliphant stepped out of it and into the waiting arms of the family.

"Are you tired, Mrs. O?" asked Father. He always called her Mrs. O.

"Not very," said Mrs. Oliphant. She turned to the Melendy children. "Look in the car."

Oliver got there first. He opened the door and stuck his head inside.

"Oh, boy," he said quietly. "Two-wheelers!"

Rush and Mona and Randy pushed against him, looking in the station wagon.

"Bicycles!" they cried almost with one voice. "Thank you, Mrs. Oliphant."

"May we practice now?" asked Oliver.

"By all means," said Mrs. Oliphant.

Rush and Mona knew how to ride. In no time at all they were racing around the driveway.

Randy was a beginner. She had a hard time learning. Her bicycle seemed to have a life of its own. It did everything to throw her off. It darted at trees and walls, and fell on its side. Rush saw her fall so many times that he decided to stop and help her.

"Look, Randy," he said, "you get on, and I'll hold the bike for you. I won't let you fall. Now, push down with your right foot, now with your left. That's it. You'll have it soon."

Thanks to Rush's help she did have it soon. In a very short time she found herself sailing happily along the drive, under her own steam.

"You're doing fine, Randy," Rush called. "How about going for a real ride?"

Oliver, who was the youngest of the Melendy children, stayed home to practice. The three others rode around the circle in the driveway. Then they started down the side of the hill and through the open gate.

Randy fell off, once when a chipmunk ran across the drive, and once when she came to the stone gate. But as soon as she was out on the road, she was able to do better, being careful to stay close to her side of the road. Mona and Rush were far ahead of her.

"Hey, wait for *me!*" called Randy.

The words were blown away from her. She raced along the road by herself. Fences flew by her, and houses, and cows, and trees, but she didn't see any of them. The road, the bicycle, the wind, were pulling her along faster and faster.

Ahead of her Mona and Rush turned to the right, and after a little while, when Randy got there, she turned too.

Then her heart leaped into her mouth!

## Trouble Ahead

A long street sloped steeply away below Randy. She saw the houses and stores on each side, and the people and the cars, and the church at the foot of the hill.  Where were Rush and Mona?

"Save me, save me," prayed Randy as the bicycle went faster and faster down the long slope.

She couldn't remember how to stop or put on the brake.  She just held on as she shot down the hill.  Clear and sharp she saw an old lady and some chickens run across the street to get out of her way.

She saw the town traffic officer watching her with his mouth open. He went by in a flash. She saw the wide blue back of a parked bus in front of her growing larger and larger.

"Save me," Randy said once again before her front wheel met the back of the bus.

Then everything was black, deep, and still.

When she opened her eyes, she was looking up at the traffic officer and the bus driver. There were a few other people around, and they were all looking at her.

"Are you all right?" asked the bus driver. "Hurt any place?"

"My head hurts," said Randy. Something warm and wet ran down her forehead.

38

Suddenly Randy jumped to her feet. "My bike!" she cried. "Is my bike all right?"

"Your bike's O.K.," said the traffic officer, "but you've got a bad cut on your forehead. My house is right across the street. You come with me, and let my wife take care of that cut."

"Hey, Randy, are you O.K.?" Rush came riding up, looking scared. Behind him she saw Mona, looking worried.

"I guess I am," Randy answered in a weak voice. Then she straightened up. "I was knocked out!" she said proudly.

The name of the traffic officer was Mr. Wheelwright. His wife, Mrs. Wheelwright, was a very friendly lady with a kind heart. She took Randy under her wing at once.

"Dear me, dear me," she said, making a clucking sound. "Why, you poor little thing. Why, you poor little thing."

39

The Wheelwrights' house was very interesting. It was full of plants and cages of birds. When they went into the bathroom upstairs, Randy couldn't believe her eyes. An alligator was in the bathtub!

"My goodness," was all she could say. The alligator was about two feet long and lay half out of the water in the tub. He had a kind of smile on his face.

Randy was so interested she hardly felt the hurt as Mrs. Wheelwright dressed her wound.

"Where did you get him, Mrs. Wheelwright?"

"My sister sent him to us more than twelve years ago. We thought the creature would die pretty soon."

She put a dressing on the cut and taped it down.

"Well, but he didn't die," she went on. "We took good care of him because after all we've got soft hearts. First thing you know he's feeling frisky as a kitten, and he's got that great big smile on his face.

"In summer Mr. Wheelwright puts him out in a tank in the yard. In winter, now that he's getting so big, we just have to keep him in the bathtub. The trouble is, we have to take our baths in the kitchen."

She smiled down at Randy.

"Now, honey, you come on downstairs and lie on the sofa for a while, and I'll find you a bite to eat. Then you can meet the rest of the family."

Were there other people in the house? Randy had heard no voices.

The rest of the family turned out to be animals. There were three big cats, a fat old dog, and ever so many birds.

Randy lay quietly on the sofa until Mrs. Wheelwright brought her a frosted doughnut and a glass of lemonade.

"My lands!" cried Mrs. Wheelwright suddenly. "Your brother and sister have been waiting outside all this time!" She made her way between the tables and chairs and sofa, then over the cats and dog to the front door.

Rush and Mona came in, looking hungry, and sat down quietly, like company.

"Are you really all right, Randy?" asked Mona as Mrs. Wheelwright hurried out to the kitchen.

"I'm fine," Randy said. "I like this place."

Soon Mrs. Wheelwright returned with more dough-nuts and lemonade. "Your little sister got a bad cut," she told Rush and Mona.

"Oh, she's always doing something," Rush answered between mouthfuls. Randy felt pleased with herself.

Then Mr. Wheelwright came in. He said that he'd drive Randy home in the next-door neighbor's pickup truck, but Randy wanted to ride her bike.

"That's right," said Rush. "After a crash they always make pilots fly again, so they won't be afraid."

Before she left, she thanked Mrs. Wheelwright. "May I come to see you sometime?" she asked.

"You come whenever you want to, honey," Mrs. Wheelwright said. "Maybe you would like to come on Thursdays when I let the birds fly around the house. Or maybe you would like to come on Saturdays when I do my baking."

"Maybe I'd like to come both times," Randy said, and Mrs. Wheelwright seemed to think that was a good idea.

Randy liked the ride home. Her bicycle seemed to be sorry for its past acts. It took her quietly in at the gate and along the drive without one fall.

"My land!" cried Cuffy, meeting her at the door.

"The town traffic officer has an alligator in his bathtub!" Randy told her.

"The *what!*" Cuffy looked surprised. "You sure your head feels all right?"

That night Randy had her supper in bed. Then everyone came up to see her. Mrs. Oliphant and Father made her promise to ride her bike only on home grounds until she became a better rider.

Before she turned out the light, Randy took a good look at her wounds. There were four dark bruises and a skinned knee on her right leg, and five bruises on her left. One arm was bruised too.

The really important wound, the best one, the wound she thought the most of, was the cut on her forehead. Maybe it will leave a scar, she thought hopefully, a fine little white scar.

She could point to the scar and say in an off-hand way, "This scar? Oh, I got this the time I ran into the back of the bus."

*Based on a story by Elizabeth Enright*

# Becky and the Bandit

## A Boy's Job

"Wake up, Becky! Wake up!"

Becky opened her eyes to see her mother bending over her bed with a tallow candle held high in one hand. Becky was very sleepy, but she smoothed her golden curls out of her eyes and tried to read her mother's face in the dancing light.

"Please, dear, try to understand me." Her mother's voice was worried.

The worry reached through into Becky's mind and made her sit up suddenly. She almost knocked the candlestick out of her mother's hand.

45

"What is it?" she asked, pushing her curls away from her face. "Isn't Father any better?"

"No," said her mother. "He can't go down the mountain after all.. You'll have to go instead."

"Me?" cried Becky. Then, remembering that her sick father might be asleep, she said softly, "Am I to take the gold to town for him?"

Mother set down the candle. "Yes, I want you to hurry now and dress for the ride. You must leave soon." Mother looked down at her small daughter for a minute.

Becky tumbled out of bed and jumped up and down as her feet hit the cold floor.

"This will be your chance to make believe you're a boy, Becky," said Mother. "You've always wished you were a boy. Now you must dress like one and act like one every step of the way. You will have to wear Simon's clothes and put your hair up under his cap."

Becky's eyes began to dance in the candlelight as she listened to the exciting plan. Holding her bright curls together all tight in one hand, she turned and smiled at herself in the looking glass. No one would ever be able to guess she was a girl if she had on her brother's clothes!

46

Becky and her family lived in the mountains east of the San Joaquin Valley many miles from town. Here her father had taken over a gold mine. With the help of his son he had washed enough gold from the earth to keep his family and even to save a little money for later years.

Now it was time to take some gold down to the town to pay the tax on the mine. But he was sick, too sick to take the long ride.

Simon, Becky's big brother, would have made the trip if he had been at home, but Simon had gone to try his luck at sea. Mother had to stay at home to take care of Father.

Becky wasn't afraid. The tax gold had to be paid, and she would do it.

# Adventure

Right in the middle of breakfast Becky's heart jumped so wildly that she bit her tongue. She might even meet Joaquin Murrieta!

Joaquin Murrieta was a bandit who, with some other bad men, traveled the roads of the San Joaquin Valley and the hills round about. He rode looking for whatever he might steal—a bag of gold in the pocket of some unlucky person, or a whole herd of cattle. Whatever Joaquin wanted, he would steal.

Just to speak his name was enough to make crying children stop their noise, and their mothers' faces grow white. Joaquin Murrieta was a real bandit, cruel and heartless.

But sometimes he could be kind too. Strange stories were told of his kindness when his heart was touched by the troubles of an unlucky person. One could never be sure how he might happen to be feeling. His acts were more often cruel than kind, so people stayed as far away from him as they could. There were many more stories of his meanness than there were of his kindness.

Now Becky was seated at her father's bedside, listening to the plan. She was told what she should do and how she should take the gold to the town tax office. She had some trouble following his words. Her thoughts were still on the exciting chance of a meeting with the bandit.

At last her father handed her a little bag which she was to carry fastened inside Simon's blue shirt.

"Go straight to the tax office," he said. "If the taxes should go unpaid, someone would have the right to take our mine. Take good care of the gold, Becky."

Becky promised herself that no one would ever get it from her, not even Joaquin Murrieta!

The dawn was beginning to show above the hills when Becky was in the saddle ready to ride. She waved good-by to Mother, then spoke to Prince. The horse stepped forward, and Becky was on her way.

It was fun to be riding like a boy instead of sideways as a lady should. Never in all her ten years had she felt so much like a boy. Every inch of her felt ready for anything, and for one minute she almost hoped she would meet Joaquin Murrieta.

The sun was up and the world awake by the time Becky reached the banks of Bear Creek. The first danger of her ride was at hand.

The creek was wider than Becky had ever seen it. She knew at one look that the middle of it would be well over Prince's back. That would mean that the horse would have to swim. Where would be the safest crossing? She did not know.

Then it came to her that Prince should know where it would be best to cross the creek. She would give him his head and let him choose his own way. Quietly she told him to go forward.

He walked carefully down the bank and into the water. Down, down he went, and the water came up. It was above his knees now, higher and higher. All at once Becky knew that Prince was swimming. His head was stretched out flat before him, and she could feel his feet working under him. She could see the other bank of the creek coming closer.

At last she felt a bump, and then Prince began climbing up the bank. They were safely across! Becky, shivering with cold, felt for the heavy lump under the blue shirt. The bag of gold was there, quite safe.

51

## Bandit's Gold

The sun was high now. Becky and Prince had both dried from their swim, and they had almost reached the valley floor. Then, rounding a hill, they met the bandit.

The minute Becky saw the horsemen all wearing guns, she knew it was Joaquin Murrieta and his men. It was easy to pick out the leader. He sat on his horse and watched her with a slow, heartless smile, while every bit of color went out of Becky's face.

At last the bandit spoke. "Good day," he said.

Becky swallowed and said nothing. Instead she galloped forward, hoping against hope that the men would part and let her ride on her way. When she came up to the leader, he put his horse across Prince's path, stopping him.

"Not so fast," he said smoothly. "You are a long way from home, my fine boy. Yes?"

Still Becky said nothing.

"And what are you doing so far from home? It is now the time for taking tax money to town. No?" The bandit was watching her.

Still Becky held her tongue, while her heart beat wildly.

"It is a little strange for a boy to be traveling these lonely roads without a good reason. I think I know your reason." His voice became suddenly hard, and his black eyes grew small and mean. "Hand over your gold."

At last Becky spoke. Lifting the reins, she shouted, "Hi," and banged her feet sharply into Prince's sides.

The horse jumped forward so suddenly that he almost got through the circle of surprised men. Almost! Then the men closed in around him, and Becky couldn't get away.

One of the men tried to pull her from the saddle, but Becky had decided to fight. They must not get Father's gold. Strongly she hit out at the dark smiling face before her. The man fell back, but another rushed his horse to her side.

In the fight which followed, Simon's old cap was brushed from Becky's head, and her curls came loose. They fell to her shoulders, shining like gold.

Becky was more frightened than ever. Now they would see that she was a girl and helpless against them. How could a girl stand off these cruel men?

Suddenly, above the noise of the horses' feet and her frightened cries, Becky heard a voice shouting, "Stop! Stop! Let her go."

The crowd fell back to let Joaquin Murrieta ride up to where Becky sat on Prince, with her golden hair bright about her shoulders.

"So you are a girl," he said, his voice gentle and full of surprise.

For a minute Becky and the bandit eyed one another. Then the man smiled a slow smile. "So! You did have gold with you after all." He was looking at her shining hair. "Never have I seen gold so beautiful, and I must have it."

"Oh, my," thought Becky, shivering with fear, "is he going to cut off my hair?"

All at once her curls, which she had never liked, seemed very, very wonderful to her.

As she watched with frightened eyes, Murrieta took a hunting knife from his belt. Moving his horse close alongside Prince, he reached for one of Becky's curls.

His men watched with interest as their leader's knife cut through one curl and he held it up for all to see. With a low bow over his saddle horn to Becky, he put the prize into his shirt pocket.

55

"I wish only one curl, *Señorita*," he said as he put his knife back into his belt. "I will not be heartless and take all your gold from you. Murrieta is not the enemy of little girls. Thank you." He signaled to his men, and they pulled their horses back. "Go now. *Adiós.*"

Becky didn't wait for Murrieta to have a change of heart. With a slap of the reins she sent Prince down the road on a wild gallop.

Late that day Becky reached the town without having to go through any more adventures. She walked into the tax office and handed over the little bag of gold. She was given a piece of paper that said the taxes were paid. The mine was safe, thanks to Becky's golden curls.

Many years later, when Becky had become an old lady, she liked to tell her grandchildren about her meeting with the bandit.

"So you see," she used to say, "it is wisest for girls to be happy always that they are girls."

But her granddaughters didn't always look as if they thought so!

*Doris Gates*

# Daniel Boone

## *What Was on the Other Side?*

"Daniel! Oh, Daniel!" There was no answer.
The woman called again. "Daniel! Daniel
Boone, where are you?" Still there was no answer.
She looked around. At last she went back into
the little log cabin. "Where can that boy be?"

Daniel Boone's mother knew very well where
her son was. There was nothing that ten-year-old
Daniel liked better than to be out in the woods.

The Boone family lived where the country was
wild. Their log cabin was set in a clearing that
had been slowly cut out from the forest. A little
of the cleared land had been plowed and planted,
but the woods were all about them. They had
few neighbors.

Daniel loved his home in the woods. He learned to walk as softly as a cat and to go through the woods without being seen. He learned to watch out for Indians.

Daniel knew which nuts and berries were good for food. He knew all the little sounds and cries of the animals that lived in the forest. He could read their tracks and tell where to look for them. He could build a fire and cook his food, and find his way about even at night.

It was a great life, and Daniel loved every bit of it. As the years went by, he grew to be a tall, strong man, but a restless one who always felt crowded when there were too many cabins and people about.

When Daniel was twenty-one years old, he fell in love with Rebecca, a pretty dark-eyed girl, and asked her to marry him. Little did Rebecca guess how exciting life would be with this tall, strong young man.

58

After Rebecca and Daniel were married, they decided to move farther back into the hills, away from the other settlers. Here Daniel took some land and built a cabin. The neighbors came over and helped him.

From the door of his cabin Daniel could see the blue tops of the mountains to the west. He liked to look at them and often wondered what was on the other side.

Then one day a stranger came to the settlement. He had just come back from a trip to the other side of the mountains.

"The land is rich," he said. "Wild game is everywhere. I have never seen a finer country."

"What is the land called?" asked Daniel.

The stranger answered, "The Indians call it Kentucky."

"Are there many Indians there?" asked Daniel.

"Yes," said the stranger, "they go there to hunt wild game. When enemy hunting parties meet there, the place becomes a battleground. Kentucky is often called the dark and bloody ground."

After Daniel talked with the stranger, he wanted more than ever to explore Kentucky. It might turn out to be a good place to settle and raise his growing family. So he made plans for a trip to Kentucky.

Daniel Boone spent several years exploring on the other side of the mountains. He hoped someday to bring Rebecca and his children there to live.

Other people were beginning to think as Daniel Boone did. They had heard many a tale of that fine land, but a road was needed on which to travel west through the wilderness.

When at last the time was ripe to cut a road through the wilderness into Kentucky, Daniel Boone led the way. His woodsmen sharpened their axes and cut down trees to widen Indian trails. They often had to fight off the Indians.

In a few months the woodsmen had cut a road through the forests and over the mountains. It was not much of a road. It was really a trail for horses. It was called the Wilderness Road, and it ended not far from a river in Kentucky.

There Daniel Boone and his men began to build a fort and some log cabins. One corner of the fort was near the river. This made it easy to get water if the settlers were attacked by Indians.

When it was finished, the men named the fort Boonesborough, after Daniel Boone.

Rebecca Boone and her daughter Jemima were the first white women to reach the new settlement. Soon other families began to arrive.

All did not go well with the settlers. There was trouble with the Indians who were fighting hard to keep their forest lands. Some of the settlers even packed up and braved the Wilderness Road again to get back to their old homes in the East.

## Jemima Takes a Dare

Jemima Boone was now almost a young lady. She had grown up in the wilderness and knew its dangers. Her father had often warned her never to go far from the fort.

"The Indians do not like us because we are pushing them from their hunting grounds," he had said. "They are fighting fiercely for their forest lands. So always stay near the fort."

Then one day some of her friends dared her to go canoeing on the river away from the fort. They said, "Jemima is afraid, afraid, afraid."

This was too much for the daughter of Daniel Boone, who had dared to cross the mountains and explore unknown lands. She took the dare and went with her friends for a canoe ride.

When the canoe came near the bank, down the river from the fort, Indians rushed out and took the girls prisoners. No one at the fort heard Jemima's cry for help or the screams of her friends.

When the girls did not return at sundown, Daniel Boone and some of the men began to look for them. After Daniel found the canoe and the tracks, he knew what had happened. So the men followed the trail as far as they could that night.

At daylight the next morning they went on. They looked for every little sign which would tell them where the Indians had gone. The girls had tried to mark the trail as well as they could. In some places they had broken off branches from the bushes along the way. They had dropped bits of cloth from their dresses to show a fork in the trail.

At last Daniel Boone and his party caught up with the Indians. Daniel asked all but three of his men to keep hidden. The three were to go with him.

Inch by inch they crept up to the camp. When they were close enough, but hidden from sight, they raised their guns and fired. Then they jumped up and ran toward the Indians, shouting and screaming. The Indians were taken by surprise. Jemima and her friends were rescued and brought safely back to the fort.

## More Exciting Years

There were many fights with the Indians that year. Daniel Boone was taken prisoner. He had been a prisoner of the Indians several times, but this was different.

The Indians pulled out part of Daniel's hair, a little at a time. At last only the hair on top of his head was left. This they made into braids. Then they put strings of beads around the braids. They painted his face and body bright colors. He was to be like a son to Chief Blackfish.

The other Indians brought presents. Red feathers were put in his braids. He was given a new name, Big Turtle.

The Indians were glad that Daniel Boone was living with them. He was a brave man and a very famous one.

Daniel lived with the Indians for months. Then he found out that they were planning to attack Boonesborough. He knew that he must warn his friends at the fort.

At last Daniel had a chance to get away. When the Indians found that he had gone, they sent their fastest runners after him, but they could not catch him.

For five days and nights he traveled. He could not take time to rest or hunt for food. The Indians were too close behind him. Only once did he stop to eat. He walked and ran more than one hundred miles until he reached the safety of the fort.

Daniel Boone began at once to get the fort ready for an attack. Soon the Indians came, but the settlers were ready for them. The battle lasted nine days. There was fierce and bloody fighting.

66

The Indians set fire to the fort, but a sudden rainstorm put the fire out. Then the Indians dug their way underground to get inside of the fort. More rain came and loosened the dirt so much that the way was blocked. When all these things happened, the Indians gave up and left.

The next few years were exciting ones. More and more people were coming to live in Kentucky. Boonesborough was no longer the only settlement.

Kentucky went right on growing and growing. Daniel Boone's many adventures with the Indians had made him one of the most famous men in America. He had done more than any other man to bring settlers to Kentucky, and to make it a safe place to live.

*Irving R. Melbo*

# If Only . . .

If only I'd some money,
    I'd buy a jolly boat
And get a pair of sea boots
    And a furry sort of coat,
A case or two of salted beef
    And a seaman's wooden chest,
And I'd sail away to the North Pole,
Or I'd sail away to the South Pole,
    Whichever I thought was best.

I'd get up very early—
    They wouldn't see me go—
Jimmy would be with me,
    But no one else would know.
Dogs are very useful,
    And I couldn't part with Jim,
And whether I went to the North Pole,
Or whether I went to the South Pole,
    It would be all the same to him.

Perhaps we'd see a mountain
    That no one else had seen;
Perhaps we'd find a country
    Where no one else had been.
Suppose we climbed an iceberg
    And saw the midnight sun!
Oh, whether we went to the North Pole,
Or whether we went to the South Pole,
    Wouldn't it all be fun?

*Rose Fyleman*

# Things to Think About and Do

1. Benjie, Sammy Andy, and Becky each wished for something important. What were their wishes? Which ones might come true someday? Which one could not come true? How does the ending of one story tell you that the wish didn't come true?

2. Each of the following things was important in one of the stories. Tell which story each one was in and why it was important.

a flashlight       a rainstorm

a lock of hair       engine trouble

a long steep hill

3. In which story did someone take a dare? What was the dare and what happened because of it? Make a list of your ideas about taking dares. Be ready to give reasons why it is unwise to take a foolish dare.

4. Who could have kept out of trouble if they had stopped to think? What should each have done instead of rushing headlong into trouble?

5. Decide which one person in these stories you think showed the greatest courage. Be ready to tell why you think so.

6. If Daniel Boone had been as interested in caves as Sammy Andy was, he might have spent much of his life exploring famous caves in Kentucky. Find out more about these caves in an encyclopedia or in other books. Make a list of words to use in describing a cave. Then plan a talk about caves, using some of the words. Be sure to practice your talk before you give it.

7. Choose something exciting that happened in one of the stories. Act out this part. Let the other children guess what story you are playing. You may wish to ask some of your friends to be in your play.

8. Make believe that you want to write a story for a newspaper about Becky's adventures with the bandits. To get the story, plan to talk with Becky. Make a list of things to ask her about the adventure.

9. Match each person with something that he did. Some did more than one of the following:

| Benjie | learned a new skill |
| Sammy | helped someone in trouble |
| Randy | took a foolish dare |
| | went exploring |
| Becky | overcame fear |
| Jemima | took over in time of need |

# Some Books to Read

*Andy's Wonderful Telescope*, by G. Warren Schloat.

Andy finds adventure in his own back yard when he explores the sky through a telescope and sees many wonderful things.

*Becky and the Bandit*, by Doris Gates.

This is the lively book from which came the story of Becky's exciting adventure.

*Brighty of the Grand Canyon*, by Marguerite Henry.

A brave little burro outwits some bandits to begin a life of freedom and adventure.

*The Courage of Sarah Noble*, by Alice Dalgliesh.

Sarah needed courage when she was left alone with the Indians in the early days of our country. A true story.

*Elephant Bridge*, by Jeffrey Potter.

A Burmese boy runs away from home and is adopted by an elephant herd in the jungle.

*Gone-Away Lake*, by Elizabeth Enright.

There is high adventure in this present-day story about a lively boy and girl who find some old houses and two company-loving old people from another time.

# Old Favorites

# The Brave Little Tailor

## Seven at One Stroke

One fine summer morning, as a little tailor sat by his open window sewing, a farmer's wife came down the street. She was calling, "Good jam! Good jam! Buy my jam!"

The little tailor put his head out of the window and cried, "Come here, my good woman. This is the place to sell your jam."

The woman climbed the three steps to his shop and uncovered the basket in which was a large jar of his favorite jam.

"That smells so good," said the tailor, "I must have a fourth of a pound."

The woman, who had hoped to sell much more, gave him what he wished and went away grumbling. The tailor spread some of the jam on a piece of bread. He placed the bread on a chair near him and began to sew, with his heart full of joy.

"Before I take even one bite," he said, "I must finish this fine woolen coat."

In the meantime the smell of the jam brought many flies to feast upon the sweet. The tailor tried to drive them away, but it was no use. So he ran to the chimney corner and got a piece of cloth.

"Wait and see what I will give you!" he cried, slashing at the flies with the cloth.

In a minute he stopped and counted. To his surprise no fewer than seven flies lay stretched out with their legs in the air. They were quite dead.

"What a fellow am I!" he exclaimed. "Seven at one stroke! The whole town shall hear of this."

Quickly the little tailor cut out a wide belt and sewed on it these words: *Seven at one stroke.* Then snipping the thread, he put on the belt.

"Why not tell the whole world about it?" he asked himself. "Why stop at this town?" He now thought himself much too brave to be a tailor.

Before leaving the house, he looked for something to take with him. All he found was a soft cheese, which he stuck in his pocket. As he went out the door, he saw a bird caught by a bright thread in a clump of bushes. This the tailor placed in his pocket with the cheese. Then he set out, light of heart and of foot.

The road he took led him up a high mountain. When he reached the top, he met a giant.

"Good morning, my friend," said the little tailor. "I am out looking for adventures. Will you go along with me?"

The giant was scornful. "Go adventuring with such a wee thing as you! A likely idea!"

"Not so fast," cried the tailor. He unbuttoned his coat and pointed to the belt. "If you can read, that will show you what a man I am."

The giant read, "Seven at one stroke," and thought it must be seven men the tailor had killed.

"Well, now I shall test you," said the giant. "Look here, can you do this?" He took up a large stone and squeezed a drop of water from it.

"Oh, that is nothing!" exclaimed the tailor.

He reached into his pocket and took out the cheese. He squeezed and squeezed until thin milky water ran out of it, crying at the same time, "Beat that, if you can."

The giant knew not what to say. However, he took up another stone, and threw it so high that the eye could hardly follow it.

"That is very clever," said the tailor, "but the stone will fall somewhere. I will throw you one that will not come down to earth again."

He put his hand in his pocket, and taking out the bird, threw it into the air. The bird soared overhead and soon flew out of sight.

"What do you think of that?" asked the tailor.

"You can throw very well," said the giant, "but can you lift as easily as you can throw?"

He led the little tailor to a forest in which lay a huge tree that had fallen to the ground.

"Now then," he said. "I'll test you again. If you are as strong as you say, just help me to carry this tree out of the forest."

"Most willingly," answered the little man. "You take the trunk on your shoulders, and I'll take the leaves. They are the heaviest."

The giant lifted the trunk on his shoulders, but the clever little tailor crouched in the branches. The giant started off, not knowing that he was carrying the tailor. He had not gone far, however, when he put down his heavy load.

78

"I cannot move a step farther," he cried. "Do you hear?"

At this the tailor jumped lightly down, seized the tree with both hands and exclaimed, "Well, you can't be so very strong. I should think you would be able to carry such a tree as this."

The giant was not happy with the outcome of the test, but he could do nothing about it just then. So he took the tailor home with him to spend the night.

Now the giant lived with many other giants in a great cave, and all the beds were huge. The little tailor didn't like the big bed where he was to sleep. When all was quiet, he crept out of it and curled up in a corner.

In the middle of the night the giant, thinking the tailor was asleep, seized an iron pole. With this he struck a blow at the bed, breaking it.

"Ah," thought he, "I must have killed the little grasshopper. He'll play no more tricks now."

The next morning, when the giants went out into the woods, the tailor walked up to them as brave as ever. It so frightened the giants to see him alive again that they took to their heels, remembering he had killed seven at one stroke.

## More Danger Ahead

The tailor traveled on until he came to the gates of the king's palace. There he lay down on the grass and went to sleep. People passing by him could see the words, *Seven at one stroke,* on his belt. They thought he must be a great soldier, and told the king. Then the king sent for the little tailor and asked him to join his household.

The tailor was given a fine apartment in the king's palace, but the other servants were afraid of him. They wished him a thousand miles away.

"What might become of us if he were angry with us?" they asked in great excitement. "He can kill seven at one stroke."

They went to the king and told him they were leaving. They would not stay with a man who could kill seven at one stroke. This worried the king, but how could he get the newcomer to leave without making him angry? At last an idea came to him, and he sent for the little tailor.

"In a forest not far from here," he told the tailor, "live two giants so fierce that no one will go into that part of my kingdom. If you can destroy these giants, I will let you marry my daughter and half my kingdom will belong to you. You shall have a hundred soldiers with spears to help you."

The tailor rode off to the forest, the hundred soldiers following after him. When they reached a cottage at the edge of the forest, he asked them to stay behind while he looked for the giants. This they were quite willing to do.

The tailor found the two giants fast asleep under a tree. He ran quickly and filled both his pockets with large stones. Then he climbed up into the tree and let fall one stone after another upon one of the giants.

The giant woke up and gave his friend a rough push. "What do you mean by hitting me?"

"You are dreaming," said the other. "I never touched you."

Grumbling, they went to sleep again, and the tailor threw a heavy stone at the other giant. He woke up in a rage.

"Now it is you who are striking me," he cried. "What do you mean by it?"

"I never struck you," the first giant growled.

As soon as their eyes were closed again, the tailor threw his largest stone at the first giant, who jumped up in a great rage and seized his friend roughly by the shoulder.

"This is too much," he cried, landing a fierce blow on his sleeping friend. So they began to fight in such a rage that they uprooted whole trees. The battle lasted until both giants lay dead.

The little tailor crept forth from the woods to the cottage where the hundred soldiers waited. "I have made an end of them both," he said.

Then the little tailor went before the king, who said, "There is a fierce unicorn in my forest. It spreads fear over the whole kingdom. You must kill this creature too."

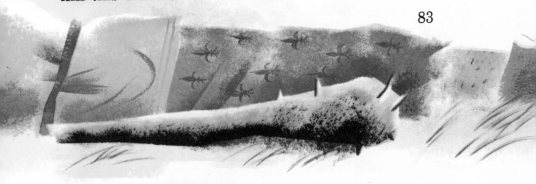

"One unicorn will be nothing after two giants," said the tailor, not the least discouraged. "Seven at one stroke, that is the way I work."

He went to the forest, taking with him a rope and an ax. The unicorn was not long in coming. As soon as it saw the tailor, it rushed forward to run him through with its one horn.

The tailor stood quite still and waited for the animal to come nearer. Then he jumped lightly behind the trunk of a large tree. The unicorn ran at the tree with all its might, sticking its horn tightly into the trunk and making itself a prisoner.

84

The tailor put the rope around the unicorn's neck, and chopped off the horn with his ax. Then he led the animal to the king.

The king still did not keep his promise. The tailor must now kill a boar that was destroying the forest. The king's hunters would help him.

Off went the tailor, the hunters following him. When they came to the woods, the little man made the others wait as before and went on alone. As soon as the boar caught sight of the tailor, it flew at him, but he was too quick for it. He jumped through the open window of a chapel that stood nearby, and out through another on the other side.

The boar was soon after him, racing into the chapel through the doorway. The tailor, now on the outside, quickly closed the door, and the wild boar found itself a prisoner, for it was unable to jump out of the chapel window.

The little tailor called the hunters and showed them the prisoner. Then he went as before to the king. This time the king had to keep his promise, and the little tailor married the princess. As king and queen they ruled over half the kingdom and lived happily ever after.

*Wilhelm and Jacob Grimm*

# The Stonecutter

Once upon a time there was a stonecutter who worked hard all day long, cutting stones with hammer and chisel. These he made into blocks for building houses and roads. It was hard work, but the stonecutter was contented until one day when he saw the king ride by.

The king was sitting in a fine carriage, and servants held a sunshade of turquoise silk with golden tassels over him.

"Oh," breathed the stonecutter, "if only I were the king, and servants held a silken sunshade over me!"

Now inside the mountain where the stonecutter was working, there lived an old wizard who heard his wish and gave it to him.

86

In the next minute the stonecutter was himself the king. He was sitting comfortably in the carriage. Servants were holding over his head the turquoise sunshade.

"Oh," he breathed happily. "Now I am the greatest of all people alive. I am the king. I shall wear a crown. I shall sit on a throne."

But one day when he was about to go on a journey, the servants forgot the sunshade, and the king had to wait in his carriage under the hot sun. And he was very uncomfortable.

"I am not, after all, the greatest thing in the world," he said. "The sun is great enough to make me uncomfortable. He is greater than I. How I wish I were the sun!"

Again the old wizard gave him his wish. The stonecutter became the sun. He shone down strongly over the land, burning the grasses and drying up the rivers. And the people hid from his fierce beams, and he was happy in his power.

But one day a cloud drifted between him and the earth, and he could not shine through it.

"The cloud is greater than the sun," said the stonecutter, who was now the sun. "Oh, if only I could be that cloud!"

The old wizard in the mountain heard his wish, and he at once became the cloud. Now he had the power to send down water upon the earth. And this he did with such might that soon the river rushed over its banks, carrying with it sheep and calves, donkeys and horses, and even people.

But one thing the water could not overcome. That one thing was a great rock which stood fast, and the water had to break and go around it.

"What!" cried the stonecutter, who was now the cloud. "Is there something more powerful than I? Oh, if only I could be that rock!"

88

In the next second the stonecutter became the rock. He held himself proudly and looked far down upon the people moving below him. Rain could not wash him away, and he was contented.

"Now," he said, "I can watch the days and years come and go."

But one day a shivery feeling went all through him. A man was hitting the rock with hammer and chisel, and pieces of the rock were being broken off and falling upon the ground.

And the stonecutter, who was now the rock, said, "Is there something more powerful than the rock? Oh, if only I could be that man!"

At once the stonecutter became that man and found himself where he had been at the beginning, breaking the rock with hammer and chisel.

"There is nothing greater than man and the work he is best able to do," said the stonecutter. Once again he was contented.

*An Oriental Tale*

89

# Bruce and the Spider

There was once a king of Scotland named Robert Bruce. He had need to be both brave and wise, for the times in which he lived were wild. The English king had stirred up trouble and discontent, and had led his soldiers into Scotland to drive Robert Bruce out of the land.

Six times had Robert Bruce led his brave men against the enemy. Six times had they been beaten in fierce battles.

At last, believing that it was useless to fight longer, his men had gone home and left him alone. He had to hide himself in the woods.

One rainy day Bruce lay on the ground inside a small cottage, listening to the patter of the raindrops on the roof above him. He was so tired and sick at heart that he was ready to give up all hope.

As Robert Bruce lay thinking, he saw a spider over his head, making ready to weave a web. He watched her as she worked slowly and with great care. Six times she tried to throw the first thin thread of her web from one beam to another. Six times the thread fell short of the beam.

"Poor thing," said Bruce, "you, too, know what it is to fail."

But the spider did not give up hope after failing six times. With still more care she made ready to try for the seventh time to weave a web. Bruce almost forgot his own troubles as he watched her patiently swing herself out upon the thin thread.

Would she fail again? No! The thread was carried safely to the beam and fastened there. The web was started.

"I, too, will try a seventh time!" cried Bruce.

Patiently he made new plans and got in touch with a few of his men. Then he sent them out with messages of hope to his unhappy people. Soon brave men came from all parts of the land to join him. There was another battle in Scotland, the English soldiers were put to flight, and their king returned to his own country.

It is said that no one by the name of Bruce would ever hurt a spider after that day. What the king had learned from the little spider was never forgotten.

*James Baldwin*

91

# Spider Webs

The spiders were busy last night;
From every fence and tree
They hung their lacy webs
For all the world to see.

The mist was busy too;
In the stillness of the night
It strung the spider webs with pearls
To catch the morning light.

One spider wove a web
Like frost on a window pane;
Another one spun a single thread
That looks like a jeweled chain.

Motionless hang the webs,
By the quiet sunbeams kissed;
A fairy world was made last night
By the spiders and the mist.

*James S. Tippett*

# Someone

Someone came knocking
    At my wee, small door;
Someone came knocking,
    I'm sure—sure—sure;
I listened, I opened,
    I looked to left and right,
But nought there was a-stirring
    In the still, dark night;
Only the busy beetle
    Tap-tapping in the wall,
Only from the forest
    The screech owl's call,
Only the cricket whistling
    While the dewdrops fall,
So I know not who came knocking,
    At all, at all, at all.

*Walter de la Mare*

93

# Windy Nights

Whenever the moon and stars are set,
 Whenever the wind is high,
All night long in the dark and wet,
 A man goes riding by.
Late in the night when the fires are out,
Why does he gallop and gallop about?

Whenever the trees are crying aloud,
 And ships are tossed at sea,
By, on the highway, low and loud,
 By at the gallop goes he.
By at the gallop he goes, and then
By he comes back at the gallop again.

*Robert Louis Stevenson*

## The Flight of Icarus

Once upon a time, when the world was young, there lived a very clever man by the name of Daedalus. Now it happened that Daedalus angered the king of the island where he lived, and was made a prisoner in a high tower.

Because he was so clever, Daedalus was able to escape from the tower, but he could not escape from the island. The king had every ship that put out to sea watched to make sure that Daedalus did not leave.

95

Daedalus was not discouraged by this. "The king may rule the land and sea," he said, "but he does not rule the air. I will try that."

Daedalus had a son, a young boy named Icarus. He called Icarus to his hiding place and asked him to gather all the feathers he could find on the rocky shore. As thousands of gulls flew over the island, Icarus soon had a huge pile of feathers.

His father then went to work. He melted some wax, shaped it into a large pair of bird's wings, and covered the wax with feathers. He pressed the smallest feathers into the soft wax with his thumb. The large ones he tied on with thread.

96

It was fun making the wings. When they were finished, Daedalus fastened them to his shoulders and found himself lifted a few feet into the air for one glorious minute. Then down he came. Filled with excitement, he made another pair of wings for his son. They were smaller than his own, but strong and beautiful.

At last one clear, wind-swept morning the wings were finished, and Daedalus fastened them to the boy's shoulders.

"Watch the birds in flight, my son," he said. "See how they soar and glide overhead. See how they beat the air steadily without fluttering. What the birds are able to do, surely we can learn to do, now that we have wings like theirs."

Soon Icarus was sure that he could fly. He raised his arms up and down. He took a swift run along the shore, beating his wings as he had seen the birds do when they wanted to fly into the air. In the next moment he was lifted above the sands and flew out over the shining water.

Daedalus watched Icarus proudly, but he was very much worried for the safety of his daring young son.

He called Icarus back to his side and put his arm around his shoulders. "Icarus, my son, we have a good chance to escape, and we are about to make our flight to freedom," he said.

"No human being has ever traveled through the air before, and I want you to listen carefully to what I am about to tell you. Remember and follow these rules for our flight.

"Do not fly too high, and do not fly too low. If you fly too low, the fog and spray will make your wings heavy and weigh you down. If you fly too high, the blazing sun will melt the wax that holds them together. Keep near me, and you will be safe."

He fastened the wings more tightly to the boy's shoulders. He thought that Icarus looked like a lovely bird, standing in the bright sun, the shining wings on his shoulders, his golden hair wet with spray, and his eyes dark with excitement.

Daedalus's eyes filled with tears, and turning away, he soared into the sky, calling to Icarus to follow. From time to time he looked back to see that the boy was safe and to watch how he used his wings in his flight.

They flew across the land to test their wings before setting out for Sicily across the dark wild sea. Farmers in the fields below stopped their work, and shepherds watched in wonder. They thought Daedalus and Icarus were gods. One of them surely must be Apollo, the sun god.

Soon father and son were ready to start out over the sea toward Sicily and freedom. Icarus, beating his great wings joyfully, felt the cool wind fill them and lift him in glorious flight. He forgot the islands and the sea below him as he flew higher and higher.

His father, flying lower, looked up and called out in fear. He tried to follow the boy, but he was heavier, and his wings would not carry him so high. He could not stop, either, because he would have dropped into the sea. He could only fly on and hope that the boy would follow him.

Up and up Icarus soared, through the soft clouds and out again into the blue sky. He was filled with a sense of glorious freedom and beat his wings wildly so that they would carry him ever higher and closer to the blazing sun.

As Icarus came nearer and nearer to the sun, the air around him grew warmer and warmer. The wax wings became soft and began to melt. Small feathers fell off and floated down, warning Icarus to stay his flight and glide to earth. But the delighted boy did not notice until the blazing sun had melted the wax that held all the largest feathers to his wings.

Icarus himself began to fall. Wildly he fluttered his arms, but no feathers were left to hold the air. Down, down he fell with one frightened cry for help.

Daedalus, having lost sight of his son, but hearing the faraway cry, called, "Icarus, my son, where are you?"

Then he turned back in time to see his son falling, straight as an arrow shot from the clouds above, into the sea. Daedalus hurried to save him, but it was too late. Icarus drowned before he could reach him. Only a few soft feathers floated on the surface of the sea.

With a sad flutter of wings Daedalus flew on, but the joy of his flight was gone. There was only grief in his heart.

When he arrived in Sicily, he went straight to the temple of Apollo. There he hung up his wings as an offering to Apollo. In the wings he pressed a few bright feathers he had found floating on the water where Icarus fell. Then he left the temple. And his heart was heavy with grief for the birdlike son who had dared to fly so high in the excitement of his freedom from the earth.

*Sally Benson*

101

# The Brahman and the Tiger

### The Players

The Brahman          The Water Buffalo

The Tiger            The Eagle

The Fig Tree         The Alligator

The Camel            The Jackal

(*The Brahman, a very wise and kindly man, is walking along a road in India when he comes upon a fierce tiger in a large iron cage. The road leads to a village at the edge of the jungle.*)

TIGER. Brother Brahman, Brother Brahman, let me out of this cage for one minute, or I shall die of thirst. I want only to get a drink of water.

102

BRAHMAN. No, I will not. The villagers caught you and locked you up because you had been eating men, and if I let you out of the cage, you will eat me.

TIGER. I promise I will not. I will never be so mean. Only let me out, that I may drink some water and return. I shall soon die of thirst.

(*The Brahman is grieved to see the tiger so thirsty, and unlocks the cage door.*)

TIGER. (*Jumping out*) Ha! Ha! I am out. Now I shall kill you first and eat you, and then drink the water.

BRAHMAN. Wait a bit. Do not be in such a hurry to kill me. Let us first ask the opinion of six. If all of them say that you are being just and fair, then I am willing to die.

TIGER. Very well. It shall be as you say. We will first ask the opinion of six.

(*The tiger and the Brahman walk along until they come to a fig tree.*)

BRAHMAN. Fig Tree, Fig Tree, hear and give judgment.

FIG TREE.   On what must I give judgment?

BRAHMAN.   This tiger begged me to let him out of his cage to get a drink of water.   He promised not to hurt me if I did so.   Now that I have let him out, he wishes to eat me.   Is it just that he should do so, or not?

FIG TREE.   I give cool shade from the hot sun to all who come this way.   When they have rested, they cut and break my branches.   Let the tiger eat the man.

TIGER.   Ha!  Ha!  I shall eat you now.

BRAHMAN.   No, Tiger, you must not kill me yet, for you promised that we should first hear the judgment of six.   Come a little farther.

TIGER.   Very well.

(*They go on their way, and after a little while they meet a camel.*)

BRAHMAN.   Sir Camel, Sir Camel, hear and give judgment.

CAMEL.   On what shall I give judgment?

BRAHMAN.   This tiger begged me to open his cage door.   He promised not to eat me if I did so. Now that I have let him out, he is going to eat me. Is that just, or not?

CAMEL.   When I was young and strong, my master took care of me and gave me good food. Now that I am old, he works me too hard and beats me.   Let the tiger eat the man.

TIGER.   Do you hear that?   Ha!   Ha!   I shall eat you at once.

BRAHMAN.   Stop, Tiger, for we must first hear the judgment of six.

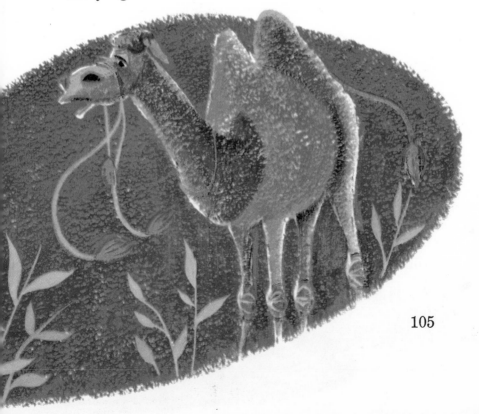

(*They both go on their way and soon meet a water buffalo.*)

BRAHMAN. Brother Buffalo, Brother Buffalo, hear and give judgment.

BUFFALO. On what must I give judgment?

BRAHMAN. I found this tiger in a cage. He prayed for me to open the door and let him out to drink a little water. He promised not to kill me if I did so, but when I let him out, he did not want to keep that promise. Is it fair that he should do so, or not?

BUFFALO. When I was able to work hard, my master took good care of me. Now that I am old, he has forgotten all I did for him. He has left me by the roadside to die. Let the tiger eat the man.

TIGER. Do you hear that? Now I . . .

(*Just then an eagle flies over the place where the three are talking.*)

BRAHMAN. O Eagle, great Eagle, hear and give judgment.

EAGLE. On what must I give judgment?

BRAHMAN. I let this tiger out of his cage. He promised not to eat me, but now he wishes to do so. Is that just, or not?

EAGLE. Whenever men see me, they try to shoot me. They climb the rocks and steal away my little ones. Let the tiger eat the man.

TIGER. (*Roaring loudly*) The judgment of all is against you. I am going to eat you.

BRAHMAN. Stay yet a little longer, for two others must be asked first.

(*After this they see an alligator.*)

BRAHMAN. Here I shall get a different answer. O Alligator, this tiger wants to eat me. I let him out of his cage on the promise that he would not do so, yet now he says he will. Is that just?

ALLIGATOR. Whenever I put my nose out of water, men try to kill me. Let the tiger eat the man. As long as men live, we shall have no rest.

BRAHMAN. But one chance more is offered me. I fear I am lost.

TIGER. Yes, I want to eat you at once. So hurry and ask this jackal, who has been standing on the bank listening.

BRAHMAN. Ah, Uncle Jackal, did you hear my story?

JACKAL. Every word.

BRAHMAN. Give then a judgment.

JACKAL. I cannot decide who is in the right until I see how it all happened and where you both were at the time. Show me the place.

(*The Brahman and the tiger return to the place where they first met. The jackal goes with them.*)

JACKAL. Now, Brahman, show me where you stood. That will help me to understand.

BRAHMAN. (*Standing by the iron cage*) Here.

JACKAL. Where was the tiger then?

TIGER. In the cage.

JACKAL. How do you mean? I don't seem able to see just how it was.

TIGER. Why, I was in the cage. Don't you see?

JACKAL. Yes, but how do you mean? How were you in the cage? Which direction were you looking?

TIGER. (*Jumping into the cage*) I stood so, and my head was on this side.

108

JACKAL.   Very good, but I still seem unable to give an opinion without seeing things just as they were.   Surely the cage door was not open?

BRAHMAN.   No, closed and locked this way. (*He closes and locks the door.*)

TIGER.   There, now you see just how things were.   Do you understand it now?

JACKAL.   Yes, and I think matters will stay just as they were.   Come, friend Brahman, let us be on our way.   Your road lies that way, I believe, and mine in this direction.

(*They go off in different directions.*)

TIGER.   And I didn't even remember to get my drink of water.

*Marion F. Lansing*

109

# Things to Think About and Do

1. How would you report the flight of Daedalus on a TV or radio program? Write down some of the things you plan to talk about under the headings below. Then make a list of pictures to show with your TV report.

     I. Where Daedalus lived
    II. Why he made the flight
   III. How he got ready
   IV. What happened on the flight

2. Write a sentence telling what made the stonecutter *contented* when he was each of the following:

    the king       a cloud
    the sun       a rock

Then write other sentences telling why the stonecutter was *discontented* after he became each of the above things.

When the stonecutter became a man again, was he at last *contented* or *discontented*? Write the reason for your answer.

3. Bring to school one or two books in which there are some favorite old tales. Then help to set up a display in the library corner.

4. Choose an old tale which you would like to share with your friends. Plan to read it aloud or retell it.

5. Think of a good reason why this unit is called "Old Favorites." If you could choose one more story for the unit, what would it be? Look through the display in the library corner and make up a new unit of five old favorites.

6. Here are some statements that characters in the stories might have made about themselves. Read each statement and tell which character might have said it. Why do you think so?

> I had to go on alone.
> I was more clever than brave.
> I was about to give up too easily.
> I had them show me just how it happened.
> I found myself back at my old job.
> Like a bird I soared ever higher.
> I wanted a fair opinion.

7. What sounds did you hear when you read "Someone"? Make a list of these sound words. What words told you how the spider's web looked in "Spider Webs"? Write these words in another list. Now make a third list of words that gave you the feeling of motion in "Windy Nights."

# Some Books to Read

*Adventure: Rare and Magical*, by Phyllis Fenner.

Just about every boy and girl should enjoy these lively tales. They are filled with the magic of adventure.

*Castles and Dragons*, compiled by the Child Study Association of America.

Those who like to meet a dragon or two in the land of make-believe will find some in this book.

*The Complete Tales of Uncle Remus*, by Joel Chandler Harris.

In this book are all the stories Uncle Remus told the little boy about the Tar Baby, Bre'r Rabbit, and the other animals. These are tales to have read aloud. They make good listening.

*The Cuckoo Clock*, by Mary Louisa Molesworth.

When the cuckoo bird asked Griselda to step inside the clock, she found a wonderful magic world there.

*The Flying Carpet*, by Marcia Brown.

This flying carpet will carry boys and girls into the world of the *Arabian Nights*.

*Household Stories*, by the Grimm Brothers.

Some of the world's favorite fairy tales are to be found here.

# Wheels and Wings

## The Family Who Had Never
## Had an Automobile

The Merry Widow was no longer young, but she was still lively. For years she had taken Doctor Brown on his rounds through the city to visit his sick patients. She waited quietly outside the houses, trying to swish the flies off her back with her short tail. You see, the Merry Widow was not a lady but a horse, and not a black one but a white one.

Samuel Brown went along on Saturdays and sat in the buggy, holding the reins while his father visited his sick patients.

114

On Sunday afternoons the whole Brown family always went to drive in the buggy. Little Susan sat on the seat between Doctor and Mrs. Brown. Mrs. Brown held Baby Brown on her knee, and Samuel sat on the floor and helped his father with the driving. So they drove happily along the quiet country roads.

"Get up!" shouted Samuel with a light tap of the reins. Sometimes the Merry Widow kicked up her heels and quite made the dust fly with her speed.

"Father," said Samuel one day, "I saw a funny looking carriage go by without any horse at all. Do you suppose our carriage would go without the Merry Widow?"

"No, Samuel," laughed Doctor Brown, "that was one of those new horseless carriage things they call automobiles. It has gears and an engine to make it go."

"They are getting to be rather a nuisance," said Mrs. Brown. "They should not be allowed on the streets to frighten our horses."

"Well, give me the Merry Widow any day," said Doctor Brown. "She takes me where I want to go."

Those funny first automobiles were always breaking down. The drivers had to get out and push or get horses to pull them home. Some of the new automobiles were called electrics. They were run by electric batteries. Others were run with steam or gasoline.

"What a fearful noise they make!" said Doctor Brown.

"What dust and smoke!" said Mrs. Brown.

"Some people are really selling their horses to buy those foolish machines," said Doctor Brown scornfully. "Such nonsense!"

The Merry Widow didn't like automobiles from the first. One day she saw one coming, and she danced down the road sideways, so that Doctor Brown could hardly hold her.

116

"Sunday driving is really impossible," said Doctor Brown, "with those monstrosities speeding down the road."

"I would rather stay quietly at home in the garden," said Mrs. Brown. "No more Sunday drives for me."

"Yes, dear," said Doctor Brown, but he was really getting worried, for it was not only Sunday drives that were growing impossible.

"The Merry Widow won't stand quietly on the street any more," he said. "As soon as I go in to visit a patient, one of those monstrosities, known as the modern automobile, comes chugging along the street and frightens her."

So poor, worried Doctor Brown visited his sick patients, with one eye on the street, wondering what on earth the Merry Widow would do next.

"I would rather have Doctor Baker," said one patient crossly. "He comes in a fine steam carriage and does not keep looking out of the window with half his attention on a horse."

117

"What shall I do?" said Doctor Brown late one afternoon.

"Why not try putting a blanket over the Merry Widow's head," said thoughtful Mrs. Brown.

"Now that's a good idea," said Doctor Brown. "Then she won't notice the machines."

The next day he tried covering her head with a small blanket. This worked very well for a while. The quieter electric and steam automobiles passed unnoticed. But pretty soon along came one of those gasoline cars, chugging down the street and making a great noise. The frightened Merry Widow danced right up onto the sidewalk and nearly upset a baby carriage.

Goodness knows how it might have ended if Uncle Hugo had not come from the country for a visit. Wearing goggles and a long duster, he drove up in his one-seated steam Locomobile. After one day in town he saw how badly things were going.

"Sam," he said to the doctor, "you'd better get a modern motor car."

"Nonsense, Hugo," Doctor Brown said with the greatest scorn.

"Yes, Sam," said Uncle Hugo, "the horse and buggy days are over."

118

"But what about the Merry Widow?" asked Mrs. Brown.

"I'll tell you," said Uncle Hugo. "The Merry Widow needs a good rest, a place to graze, and country air. What is more, I am tired of changing tires and having my car break down on muddy country roads. What I need is a good old horse."

"Then why couldn't we trade?" suggested Samuel.

"Samuel, my boy," said Uncle Hugo, "that is just what I was about to suggest. A horse belongs in the country, while an automobile is a city machine. It belongs in town."

"Well," said Doctor Brown, "I believe you're right, Hugo. Let's go and look the Locomobile over, anyway."

The whole Brown family went out to see the new steam automobile with its shiny fenders.

119

"It hardly seems big enough for all of us," said Mrs. Brown.

"Oh, yes, Mother," said Samuel, "I can sit on the back."

The upshot of the matter was that Uncle Hugo drove the happy Merry Widow off to the country, leaving the fine Locomobile for the Brown family, who had never had an automobile.

So the time came for the Brown family to take their first Sunday drive. Mrs. Brown and Susan wore their long dusters and tied on their big hats. The whole family put on goggles to keep the dust out of their eyes, and off they went.

"Not too fast, Sam, please," said Mrs. Brown.

"Yes, dear," said Doctor Brown as the little car chugged down the street.

120

"Hold on tight," called Mrs. Brown to Samuel in back, for they were going over some big holes in the street.

The automobile steamed along the road, the dust flew, and the Browns were too happy for words.

Suddenly they met a family driving in a horse and buggy.

"See the funny old horse," cried Susan. But when they tried to pass, the poor old horse danced sideways almost into the ditch.

"What a nuisance these horses are!" said Mrs. Brown after they had passed.

"They should not be allowed on the road," said Doctor Brown. "They will make Sunday driving quite impossible."

You see, though the Brown family had never had a car before, they had quite forgotten about the Merry Widow. What is more, the Merry Widow had forgotten about them. On Sunday afternoon she grazed in a green pasture, and sometimes kicked up her heels. She didn't even know that the Brown family were happily taking their Sunday drive in one of those monstrosities, the modern automobile.

*Hildegard Woodward*

121

# Twelve Seconds

## *At Kitty Hawk*

On December 12, 1903, sea gulls were flying and screaming above the lonely sands at Kitty Hawk. Inside a shed two men were working on a motor, out of hearing of the screaming gulls. The two men were Orville and Wilbur Wright.

"We have been here at Kitty Hawk more than two months," Orville was saying. "Now it is December, and we are still on the ground, waiting to try out the flying machine."

122

The brothers thought back over the past two months. First there had been the great storm that almost destroyed their shed. Next there was trouble with the motor they had made back home in their bicycle shop. Something always seemed to keep them from going up.

Everything had been carefully planned. The flying machine would take off from a track. Under the machine were skids that looked like sled runners. With these skids the machine would be kept upright on the track for the first part of the take-off. Before it reached the end of the track, the machine would be in the air.

The long track that the brothers had made could be used either on level ground or on a hill and could be moved from place to place. But it took more than two men to move the track. Orville and Wilbur needed help to set it up and to get the flying machine in and out of the shed.

Not far from the brothers' camp was a lifesaving station, where several men worked. These men had been over many times to see the flying machine.

They had said, "Just run up a flag if you ever need us to help you. We'll come right over." Orville and Wilbur had promised to call them.

123

"I think we can get the plane ready to fly today," Orville said as he worked that December morning.

Morning turned into noon, and noon passed into afternoon. When the plane was ready to fly, the sun was going down. The evening shadows were long. It was too late to make the test that day.

On the morning of December 13 the weather was good for a take-off. The sun was bright and the wind speed right.

"But this is Sunday." Wilbur spoke thoughtfully.

The brothers had grown up in a home where Sunday was always spent quietly. Their father had often said, "Sunday was made by God to be a day of rest and prayer."

So they did not fly on that perfect Sunday morning. Instead, the brothers waited quietly all day, watching the clouds throw shadows over the long, lonely stretches of sand.

They made another try on December 14, but the plane was damaged only three seconds after it left the track. It took them two days of hard work to repair the damage.

Everything was ready on the evening of December 16. If only the weather was good the next morning!

124

When they awoke early on December 17, there was a strong wind blowing across the sand. Thin ice covered the little puddles of water.

Orville went outside the shed to test the wind. In a few minutes he was so cold that he had to go back inside the shed to get warm.

At seven o'clock the brothers were standing by the stove in the shed. They were trying to decide if they should put off a test flight because of the strong wind.

Two hours later the wind was blowing harder than before, and at ten the wind had not gone down.

Still the brothers would not give up the idea of making the test that would tell if their years of work had been successful.

"I can't wait any longer," Orville said as he walked back and forth.

"I can't either," said Wilbur. "Let's put up the flag that will tell the men at the lifesaving station we are ready for the test."

Orville went out into the cold wind and ran up the flag. In a few minutes four men and a boy were there. Orville and Wilbur opened the shed doors. The five helpers and the two brothers pulled the machine outside.

125

## History in the Making

"We can put the track down right here on the level sand," Wilbur said. "We don't need to try the test from a hill. We will face the machine into the wind. That will help on the lift."

The men put the track down and carefully lifted the plane into place. The brothers made sure everything was working perfectly.

Overhead the gulls were wheeling and crying. It seemed as if they knew a strange new bird was going to try its wings in their sky.

Orville climbed on the wing of the plane and stretched out, face down. Then he fastened a strap around his waist. This strap would keep him from rolling off the wing.

126

Wilbur started the motor.

From a safe distance the five helpers were watching. One man said, half aloud, "All that thing needs is a coat of feathers to make it fly."

"Ready?" Wilbur called above the wind and the noise of the motor. He was standing beside the plane, holding onto the side of the wing.

127

"Ready!" came Orville's answer. His feet were hanging out behind the wing, and his hands were gripping the handles.

Slowly the plane started down the track, slowly heading into the wind, now faster . . . and faster. The wings began to lift . . . twelve inches off the ground . . . now two feet into the air.

Wilbur ran beside the plane. Someone took a picture—the first picture in history to show a plane flying in the air.

With the wind blowing harder than ever, the plane kept climbing. Now it was ten feet off the ground and still in the air. Now it was flying right away from Wilbur.

The boy who had been watching jerked off his cap and waved and shouted, "He's flying! He's flying!"

Orville did not hear. He was too busy trying to steer the plane and to think of what was happening. The machine was moving forward and up into the air away from the ground.

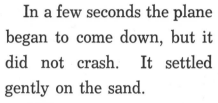

In a few seconds the plane began to come down, but it did not crash. It settled gently on the sand.

Wilbur ran to the plane.

Orville was unstrapping himself and crawling off. "How long was I up?"

Wilbur looked at the stop watch. "Twelve seconds!"

"How far did I fly?"

They both measured the distance—one hundred and twenty feet!

129

The flight had been over level land. The plane had gone up into the air and had kept going forward without lessening its speed.

Next it was Wilbur's turn to fly. This time the plane went even farther, as he gripped the handles and tried to steer it.

Orville could hardly wait for a second turn. Twenty minutes after Wilbur's flight, Orville was up in the air again. This time, to their delight, the plane stayed up longer and flew nearly two hundred feet.

At noon Wilbur was ready to make his second flight. Orville watched as his brother took off.

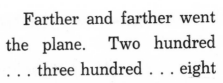

Farther and farther went the plane. Two hundred . . . three hundred . . . eight hundred feet . . . and more! Then slowly and gently the plane came down on the sand.

Orville ran to Wilbur, who was climbing from the wing. The two brothers looked into each other's eyes with smiles. The first successful powered flight had been made!

Orville and Wilbur looked at their plane and thought of the distance it had covered that day. They could not guess that someday men would make giant airplanes so large that the wingspread would be as wide as the distance of that first flight.

A lone gull screamed overhead. It dived down toward the plane on the sand.

Orville looked up at the bird. He spoke half aloud, half to himself, "You are no longer the master of the sky. Now we, too, can be riders of the air."

The sea gull made a wide circle overhead and then drifted away across the lonely sands, out over the sea.

*Madge Haines and Leslie Morrill*

131

# Success for Little Blacknose

## *What's the Matter?*

Blacknose was a locomotive. He was one of the first locomotives ever built in America. He was not very large, but he could pull five coaches, and that was five times as much as a horse could pull.

The day he made his first run with the coaches behind him had been a great day for little Blacknose. He had been named the *DeWitt Clinton* after a famous man of that time, and many famous people had traveled in his coaches.

Now it was six weeks later, and a day in the early fall of 1831. Little Blacknose did not know that, and he would not have cared if he had known it. But he did know that something had waked him up very early. There was a roaring outside his shed.

132

At first he could not understand what made the noise. But pretty soon, as he listened and wondered, he knew it came from hundreds of people all shouting together. He had never heard so many before, never in his whole engine life! Then he noticed that John Bull was gone.

John Bull was a big locomotive who had just been brought from England. He was much bigger and stronger than little Blacknose, and he was very proud of himself. He was so big that little Blacknose hardly dared to say hello to him.

"They have taken him out and left me," thought Blacknose. "It's his big day, and I'm out of it!" Poor little Blacknose! He felt as if he never could get his steam up again.

The shouting grew louder and louder. Little Blacknose could only hear. He could not see what was going on. He had remained in his dark shed for hours and hours, or so he thought.

"No wood! Not even a nibble of coal! No water! No breakfast!" he scolded.

He was getting very hungry. It was the first time he had not been cared for, needed, and used.

Suddenly he heard, "Uh-huh, I guess you'll not be so stuck up now!"

It was the old gray horse sticking his homely nose through the window of the shed and making fun of poor little Blacknose. With a loud neigh he went on, "I suppose they'll take you out still— sometimes—on rainy days." A minute later the window was empty.

Then a crew of men came rushing into the shed. They began to push and pull at little Blacknose.

"What can they want with me?" he sadly wondered. And sudden fear shot through his pipes and boiler. He guessed—he knew! They were taking him out for the crowd to laugh at! They would stand him up beside the great new engine from England, and everyone would laugh at him.

He wouldn't go. He couldn't go! If only he could stay unnoticed in his small, dark shed! He tried to keep his wheels from turning! It was no use. They were running him out now into the middle of the shouting crowd. He wouldn't look. He couldn't! Then he noticed the English engine.

A little distance down the track stood John Bull with his steam all up. Flowers were hanging around his huge smokestack, and he looked very great and grand. He had ten bright coaches hooked on behind him, but they were all empty!

134

"Why doesn't he go? Why are all the people outside the coaches? What is the matter with him?" Blacknose wondered.

Then David Mathew, his own engineer, came pushing his way through the crowd.

"Will even David laugh at me?" thought Blacknose. A little fear gnawed at him.

But no, David placed a loving hand on the cold boiler of the little engine.

135

"Fill her up, men," he said to the crew of workmen beside him. "We shall have to use the *DeWitt Clinton* after all."

What a roar went up from the huge crowd!

"Hurrah for the *DeWitt Clinton!*" they cried. "Hurrah for the little American engine! Hurrah, hurrah, hurrah!"

At last little Blacknose dared to look at the crowd. Why, they weren't laughing at him at all! They were cheering and waving. They were shouting for him, just as they always used to do.

For a minute he felt as if a large, fat piece of coal had got stuck in his supply pipe. A second later real pieces of coal were falling fast into his poor, empty little firebox. Real shining pieces of coal to give him the spark of life he needed!

136

"Breakfast, breakfasssssst, breakfasssssssst!" he hissed happily. His steam was coming up.

It was the new engine's big day, but they had had to send for him.

"Breakfast, breakfasssssst, breakfasssssssst!"

What was the matter with the English engine? Couldn't it go? He knew it had run before, when they gave it a try. He had seen it himself—big and proud and noisy.

"Well, anyway, it isn't going now," he thought. "Sssssee the empty coachchch-esssss!" he hissed.

What were they doing now? They were taking the coaches from John Bull, all ten of them. Three of them were hitched on to Blacknose. Now they were leading up seven horses. Each horse was fastened to one of the seven other coaches. The excursion train was ready, and he was at its head!

137

How the people rushed to squeeze into the three coaches behind little Blacknose! What a shouting and pushing there was! The little engine looked back proudly along his train of three.

"All the great people of the land are riding behind me," he noticed. "Only the near-great ride behind the horses."

"Toot, toot, toot, toot!" Such a blowing of the whistle in double-quick time! "Hurrah, hurrah!" Such a shouting from the passengers!

And they were off at last! Just as his wheels began to turn, Blacknose heard an excited neigh from the homely gray horse, who was fastened to the first coach behind his three.

"If it weren't for you, I'd get to Schenectady first!" the old gray horse neighed. But little Blacknose only laughed.

"Choo, choo, choo! Chew your own smoke!" he cried. "Pretty soon you won't be able even to smell mine! You haven't a ghost of a chance. Choo! Choo! Choo!"

Then he noticed the big English engine, looking very sad, and he saw that the flowers around his big smokestack had started to fall to pieces. Fortune had not smiled on him today.

138

## Such Speed!

"T-double Y-ditty. Off for Schenectady!" sang little Blacknose. "T-double Y-ditty."

The wind whistled over his smokestack. The sound of his wheels echoed on the rails, frightening the grazing cattle. The trees flew by. The rails gleamed ahead of him. He had never gone so fast before. Happy as a lark he sent a spray of jet black smoke toward the sky.

In just forty-six minutes he stood puffing and blowing at the Schenectady end of his track. Now everybody cheered him as they climbed out of his yellow coaches.

139

"It's the greatest day of my life!" he heard one man say. "I never rode so fast before."

"Such speed!" said another, straightening his tall hat. "Only forty-six minutes from Albany!"

"But where are the horses?" asked a third, speaking to David Mathew.

"I don't see them, sir," answered David, as he looked back along the gleaming rails.

Where were the horses? Twenty-nine minutes later the first of the horses climbed slowly up the last hill and pulled his coach up beside little Blacknose's train of three coaches. It was the old gray horse—all out of breath and oh, so tired!

"So you wanted to get ahead of me! What do you think of engines now?" puffed little Blacknose.

But this time the poor old horse didn't even look at little Blacknose. He closed his eyes and dropped his homely head.

When the other horses and coaches had arrived, Blacknose saw the passengers all go off toward Schenectady with the people who had come to meet them.

"They're off to get their coal and water, I suppose," the little engine thought. In two hours he saw them all come back again. The excursion train was ready for the return trip to Albany.

Never had he run so well. In just thirty-eight minutes he was back at the Albany end of his track, puffing hard but feeling very proud.

"My word!" cried David Mathew, as he climbed down from the little engine. "We've been going nineteen miles an hour."

"Nineteen miles? Wonderful!" said one of the great men. "I have never known such speed!"

"Hurrah for the *DeWitt Clinton!*" cried all the passengers. "Hurrah for our own American engine! It can go nineteen miles an hour!"

All this time the locomotive from England stood quiet and unnoticed nearby. He looked very sad, Blacknose thought, and he almost felt sorry for him. Then suddenly he found that the English engine was talking to him. He had only a little steam left, so his voice throbbed, throaty and low.

141

"Very-kind-of-you," John Bull was saying. Little Blacknose could just make it out.

"I didn't know we had met," puffed back Blacknose. But the minute he said it, he was sorry. The poor English engine looked so sad!

"Sorry-I-was-mean. Very-thankful-now," he said. "You-saved-my-excursion."

"Oh, don't thank me," Blacknose said. "I've had the run of my life! By the way, what's wrong with you, anyway?"

"Something-wrong-in-mah-supply-pipe," John Bull answered. "Couldn't-repair-me. Must-have-muffed-it-badly. Don't-understand-strangers-over-here. I'm-English-you-know!"

"Oh, are you?" said Blacknose. Why, the Englishman was a pleasant fellow, after all! "Well, I'll be glad to help you any time you need me. I hope your supply pipe will be better soon."

Little Blacknose was very happy as they ran him away to rest.

"Success, successsssssssss, successsssssssss!" he hissed gently, letting off steam.

As for the homely old gray horse, he hadn't even come in sight!

*Hildegarde H. Swift*

142

## B's the Bus

B's the Bus,
The bouncing Bus,
   That bears a shopper store-ward.
It's fun to sit
In back of it
   But seats are better forward.
Although it's big as buildings are
   And looks both bold and grand,
It has to stop obligingly
   If you but raise your hand.

## J's the Jumping Jay-Walker

J's the jumping Jay-Walker,
   A sort of human jeep.
He crosses where the lights are red.
   Before he looks, he'll leap!
Then many a wheel
Begins to squeal,
   And many a brake to slam.
He turns your knees to jelly
   And the traffic into jam.

*Phyllis McGinley*

143

# The Chopper

## *Waiting for the Helicopter*

It was late afternoon. A man and a boy stood waiting on the flat roof of a large building. The building was the Merchandise Mart in Chicago.

"He's late, Dad," said the boy. "Has he forgotten about us?"

Mr. Hardy laughed. "No, John, Bob wouldn't forget your first ride in a helicopter."

They both looked up into the cloudy sky. It had been snowing off and on all day.

"It's not a very good evening for flying," Mr. Hardy said.

"But isn't a helicopter safe in weather that wouldn't be safe for an airplane?" John asked.

"Yes, choppers are safe," answered his father slowly. "I am sure that Bob won't take us up if there is any danger."

"Why are they called choppers?" was John's next question.

"I'm not sure," said his father thoughtfully, "but I suppose it's because they look as if they were chopping at the sky. Some people call them egg beaters."

John looked around him at the roof. He didn't see how a helicopter could land on it.

Right in front of him he saw a yellow circle, like a target, painted on the roof.

"That's the target on which the helicopter will come down for the landing," his father said.

Bob, the pilot, had picked up Mr. Hardy before. This evening they were going to give John his first ride. So John and his father had come into the city together. John had brought a book with him and read while his father was busy at his office in the Merchandise Mart. Now they were waiting on the roof for the helicopter.

145

Suddenly John heard a sound different from all the others that were coming up to him from the street. This sound couldn't belong to a diesel train, or a steam train, or a car, or a truck. It must be the helicopter. He turned to look in the direction of the airport. It was from there that Bob was coming to pick them up.

All at once the helicopter came into sharp outline from the cloudy wall of sky. It was coming fast. John could see how brightly it was painted. He could see, too, how it was tilted forward, with a tail rotor sticking out behind.

The helicopter wasn't headed for John, but made for the west end of the building. It flew along in a hurried, businesslike way. Then almost as if it had suddenly remembered something, it stopped a few feet out there to the west. It stopped short in its rush and hung in the air as if it had just seen John.

For a second the helicopter hung there. Then it changed direction and came slowly toward the waiting man and boy. The circling red light on the top of the cabin shone inside. There sat Bob in the middle of a seat wide enough to allow another person on either side of him.

The helicopter came on over the roof. It stopped a couple of feet above the yellow circle and then dropped gently down. The landing skids touched right on the target.

Bob cut the throttle, and the engine made much less noise. The huge rotor blades above the cabin kept right on turning. Bob opened the door, and John and Mr. Hardy got in beside him.

147

# The Chopper Takes Off

"Weather seems a little rough," said Mr. Hardy after they were both settled comfortably inside the cabin.

"Not bad—not yet, anyway," Bob said. "We might have a little trouble finding our way, though. Let's see, where shall I drop you off?"

"Not on the front lawn," said John, playing up to Bob's joke. It sounded pretty funny to him to be "dropped off" out of the sky. "There's a tree on our lawn every five feet."

"I wasn't joking," said Bob. "I could drop you off most any place. I don't need a long runway to make a landing."

"I noticed that," said John.

"Suppose you drop us off at the airport where you always do, Bob," said Mr. Hardy. "I asked my wife to meet us there."

"Good," said Bob. "Let's go."

He gave the helicopter the throttle and the roar of the engine grew louder. The swiftly circling rotor blades stepped up their speed.

"You're going to get a funny feeling when we go off the edge of the roof," he told John.

148

He raised the pitch lever at the side of the seat. The rotor blades bit into the air as the lever moved up. Like magic, the helicopter rose two or three feet above the roof. John thought it was like being in a glass elevator.

Watching closely, John noticed that Bob pressed forward a little on the stick between his knees. This tilted the rotors so that the helicopter moved forward just enough to keep the wind from blowing it back.

The helicopter rose straight up five or six feet. That was more than enough to clear the brick-and-stone fence at the edge of the roof.

149

Suddenly John exclaimed, "Wow! That's a long way down."

It was. As soon as they passed over the edge of the roof, the distance down suddenly changed from a few feet to more than twenty stories. John felt as if he were hanging in space.

Though he had been up in airplanes several times, he had never felt like this before. Sitting out here in space with the whole side of the Merchandise Mart below him, was like nothing else he had ever known. It took his breath away.

150

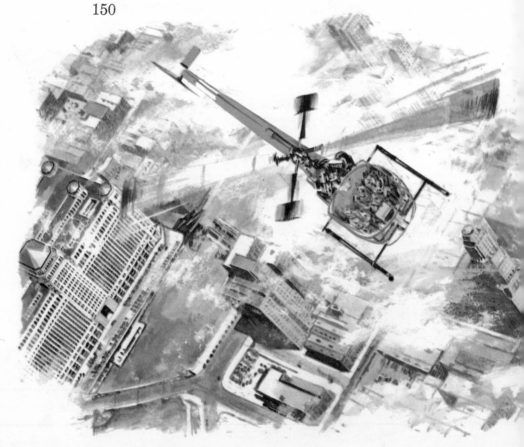

"I told you," said Bob, smiling at him. "Want to go back?"

"No, sir!" John exclaimed. "This is great!"

Bob headed west across the heart of Chicago. They could see straight down and forward for about six blocks.

"Bob," said John, "What would happen if we should run into rough weather?"

They were flying over the city at 75 miles an hour.

For answer, Bob came to a stop within little more than one hundred feet. For a second they just hung there while Bob talked about the safety of helicopters.

"If we still have power—if the engine is still working—and the weather should get rough, we could inch our way along. We could go forward at five or ten miles an hour. We could fly straight up, straight down, or sideways. We could fly safely at slow speeds and land on almost any small, open space."

Bob put the speed back to 75 miles an hour and stopped talking about helicopters. He had his eyes on the ground looking for landmarks. As they moved west from Chicago, the weather was getting rougher instead of better. All at once he caught sight of the landmark for which he was watching.

"Now I know exactly where I am," he said. "The airport is about ten miles from here."

They passed a building with a sign that John could easily read. Now he knew exactly where they were, too. A minute ago he hadn't been sure. Things look very different from way up in the air. Then he spotted the airport.

"Here we are," he shouted and pointed down.

Bob nodded. "I think I'll pick up some gasoline before I go on."

He made a tight turn and headed for the gasoline pump. He set the chopper down six feet away from it, cut the throttle, and opened the door of the cabin. John and his father got out.

"Good to have you aboard, John," Bob called down to him.

"Can't you stop long enough to have dinner with us?" asked Mr. Hardy.

152

"Thanks a lot," said Bob, "but we may get some freezing rain later this evening. So I think I'd better travel before the weather gets any rougher."

"Thank you for the fine ride, Bob," John called up to him. "It was great."

"We'll do it again soon," promised Bob, and John and his father hurried off to where Mother was waiting in the family car.

*John Lewellen*

# Cockpit in the Clouds

Two thousand feet beneath our wheels
The city sprawls across the land
Like heaps of children's blocks outflung,
In tantrums, by a giant hand.
To east a silver spire soars
And seeks to pierce our lower wing.
Above its grasp we drift along,
A tiny, droning, shiny thing.

The noon crowds pack the narrow streets.
The el trains move so slow, so slow.
Amidst their traffic, chaos, life,
The city's busy millions go.
Up here, aloof, we watch them crawl.
In crystal air we seem to poise
Behind our motor's throaty roar—
*Down there, we're just another noise.*

*Dick Dorrance*

154

# To the Moon and Back

## *A Vacation in Space*

It was the summer of 1985. Keith Hampton's vacation was just beginning, and he was wondering what he would do with it.

"Vacation won't be any fun without Dad," he told his mother.

Keith's father was chief engineer of the outer space experiments. Just now he was on Moon Base. He had been there for nearly a year finishing some experiments. No one knew for sure just when he would come back.

"I wish Moon Base had never been thought of," said Keith.

His mother laughed. "Only a few months ago you were the most excited boy in town because your father had been named to head the big experiment there," she said.

"Well," grumbled Keith. "I didn't know he was going to be away so long."

Mrs. Hampton looked suddenly very sad, and Keith was ashamed of himself.

"I miss him, too," she said. "But a great man, like your father, can't spend all his time inside his own four walls."

"I'm sorry, Mother," said Keith, trying to look cheerful. "I'm proud of Dad, same as you are. I won't grumble because outer space needs him more than we do."

The very next day the message came. It was from Chief Engineer Hampton on Moon Base. "I shall be returning to earth in a couple of weeks. Have asked to have Keith join me for my last two weeks here."

"Yippee!" shouted Keith when his mother finished reading the message. "What a vacation! Two weeks on the moon with Dad!"

156

# The Trip to the Space Station

The next day Keith started on his journey to the moon. The first part of the flight was to the space station which traveled through space between the earth and the moon. This part of the trip was made in a rocket ship, a ferry it was called.

"Put on your space suit, and then I'll strap you into your seat," the co-pilot told Keith as they got ready to take off.

The suit was a heavy thing to put on and not very comfortable. A plastic helmet covered Keith's head. At first he could hear nothing. Then he turned on the radio which was part of the plastic helmet, and he could hear everything that went on inside the rocket-ship ferry.

After the take-off the seat tilted back so that Keith stretched out flat. In a few minutes he had reached the space station. Keith soon met the men stationed there, and they showed him around the place.

Though he had heard his father tell about the space station, it was even more wonderful than he had dreamed it could be. Most of all Keith liked to look down at all the gleaming white clouds between him and earth.

## The Atomic Space Ship

Keith had to wait for several hours at the space station while the men filled the hydrogen tanks of the atomic space ship. It was fastened to the space station by a short plastic-tube bridge.

To board the space ship the passengers went through this plastic tube. Keith stopped and looked at it before stepping inside.

"I don't like this much," he said.

"What's wrong with it?" asked the pilot.

"It's too open," said Keith. "Why did it have to be made out of plastic? There's a lot of space out there." He nodded toward the gleaming stars. "I'd just as soon not be able to see all that space while I walk through it."

Keith could feel goose bumps along his back as he took his first step into the tube. It was exactly like hanging in space. He couldn't get the feel of anything under him or around him. The earth seemed very, very far away. Outside the tube the stars were very, very bright.

"Hurry it up," said the pilot, and Keith started along the tube.

When at last he found himself inside the space ship, he breathed easier. At least the ship's sides kept out that feeling of empty space!

Keith was told that another ferry was being carried inside the space ship. When they came within the moon's orbit, those who wanted to get to the moon would go aboard this ferry. Then it would be dropped from the space ship's hull. Keith wouldn't have to walk through another plastic tube!

It all happened just as Keith had been told it would. When they came to the moon's orbit, Keith and two others were put aboard the ferry. Then it was dropped from the hull of the space ship.

# Moon Base

The ferry landed on a flat surface. The sky looked much as it had from the space ship. There was the same blackness, the gleaming stars, and the shining earth far off in the sky.

His father was waiting to welcome him. Keith forgot that now he was almost twelve years old. He ran straight into his father's arms in full sight of everybody.

"It's so quiet here," Keith said, looking around.

"That's because there aren't any children on the moon," his father said. "At least there weren't until a few minutes ago."

Once inside Moon Base, Keith took off his space suit and helmet. It felt good to breathe dry, cool air again. Suddenly a thought came to him.

"I know that the moon doesn't have air around it," he said to his father. "How come we can breathe?"

"We make our own air and keep pumping it into Moon Base," Mr. Hampton said. "When you go outside, you have to carry air with you."

The Base turned out to be a very comfortable place. There was good food for dinner that evening. After dinner Mr. Hampton asked Keith to play a game of Ping-pong with him. Keith liked the idea, so his father led him to the game room. There Keith saw the largest Ping-pong table he had ever seen. It was at least thirty feet long.

"How can we ever play on that?" he asked.

His father laughed. "You'll see."

162

It was like playing in a strange dream. Though Keith drove the ball quite fast, it would fall to the table only in a very long flat curve. He kept hitting his father's returns well over the edge, and had to learn to play all over again. That was because the moon did not pull things toward it as fast as the earth did. The earth would have pulled the Ping-pong ball down faster. On the moon it came down more slowly.

Mostly, life at Moon Base was work. The men had to work just to keep alive. They had to make their own air and water. Then there was the exploring for uranium as well as the trips to the mountains on the moon.

One day Mr. Hampton took Keith for a ride in one of the tractors. These moon tractors looked like great glass balloons on tracks. Keith did not need to wear his space suit as the tractor had fresh air inside it.

On the way back from the uranium mine to the Base they stopped to look at a marker. It stood all by itself, not far from the Base.

"That marks the spot where Moon-Rocket I landed," Mr. Hampton told Keith.

The boy's eyes brightened. Our first landing on the moon happened right here!

164

"Where is the ship now?" Keith asked. He knew the crew had not returned to earth in it, because they were rescued by Moon-Rocket II.

"I'll show you when we get back to the Base," Mr. Hampton said.

Back at the Base, he took Keith to a room which was being used as a kind of living room.

"This," he said, "was the cabin of Moon-Rocket I. The whole Base has slowly grown from it, like a tree from a seed. A room was built here, a wing there, as more and more rocket ships arrived. Moon-Rocket I was taken apart. Its hydrogen tanks, hull, and so forth were used to build the Base. Moon-Rockets III and IV had the same thing happen to them, but II was sent to a museum on earth. Now do you see?"

Keith did see, and he spent a very exciting vacation at the Base while Mr. Hampton finished his uranium experiments.

Keith was happy to be returning to earth when at last the two weeks were over. It was wonderful to have Dad going back with him!

Again he climbed aboard the ferry which took them to the atomic space ship waiting on the edge of the moon's orbit. Aboard it they traveled to the space station.

When at last they arrived, the walk through the plastic tube didn't seem nearly so frightening to Keith as it had the first time.

"I guess you can get used to anything," he told himself. "Even outer space!"

A rocket ship was waiting for them, and in a matter of minutes they were back on earth again. Mrs. Hampton was at the space port to welcome the returned travelers.

"Did you have a wonderful time?" she asked.

"It was great," answered Keith. Suddenly he let out a wild shout.

"What on earth . . . ?" began Mrs. Hampton.

"I just thought of something," said Keith. "I'm going to go down in history, I bet."

"If they don't lock you up somewhere first," said his father. "One more shout like that could do it."

"Just think!" Keith said. "I've made history! I'm the first tourist ever to visit the moon!"

*William F. Temple*

# Night Plane

The midnight plane with its riding lights
looks like a footloose star
wandering west through the blue-black night
to where the mountains are,
a star that's journeyed nearer earth
to tell each quiet farm
and little town, "Put out your lights,
children of earth.   Sleep warm."

*Frances Frost*

# Things to Think About and Do

1. From the list of words below choose the one that you think best describes how each character felt in the following sentences. Write on a sheet of paper the letter in front of each sentence and the word that describes the character's feelings.

a. "I think we can get the plane ready to fly today," said Orville Wright.

b. "He's flying! He's flying!" the boy shouted.

c. "Uh-huh, I guess you'll not be so stuck up now," said the old gray horse.

d. "All the great people of the land are riding behind me," thought Little Blacknose.

e. "T-double Y-ditty," sang Little Blacknose.

f. "What on earth!" exclaimed Mrs. Hampton.

| | | |
|---|---|---|
| excited | proud | scornful |
| surprised | hopeful | happy |

2. Suppose you were in a helicopter high above your school. Make a picture map showing how the school and schoolgrounds would look from the air. Use a large sheet of paper pasted on a light piece of cardboard. Be ready to describe how things looked from high in the air.

Let a committee choose the best map to display on the bulletin board.

168

3. Make a time line of travel by air. Begin with a picture of the Wright brothers' airplane. Then show a plane like the one in the story of Benjie. Bring the time line up to the present with a picture of a jet and go beyond the present with a rocket ship.

4. Plan a dictionary of words that are used to tell about different ways to travel. You may want to make pictures to go with some words in your dictionary. Add new words as you discover them.

5. As a radio announcer you are about to report Keith's flight to Moon Base. List the three ways he traveled on his journey from the earth to the moon. Write the sentences you will use to begin and to end your report.

6. Plan a talk on outer space. Find out more about it in the encyclopedia or in books about space travel. Make a list of words to use in describing travel to other planets. Add these words to your new dictionary.

7. Look in newspapers and in magazines for pictures and stories about space travel. Post them on the bulletin board or make a book about the latest discoveries.

# Some Books to Read

*The Early Days of Automobiles,* by Elizabeth Janeway.

This book tells the whole story of automobiles and why they are as they are.

*The First Book of Space Travel,* by Jeanne Bendick.

Adventure into space awaits within this book.

*Freight Train,* by William Bunce.

This is the story of the railroads and the freight they carry. A freight train is described from engine to caboose.

*The Helicopter Book,* by Henry Lent.

Here is more about helicopters and how they are used.

*Ride on the Wind,* by Alice Dalgliesh.

The story of Charles Lindbergh's flight alone across the Atlantic Ocean is retold from his book about *The Spirit of St. Louis.*

*Riding the Rails,* by Elizabeth Olds.

Trains are on parade in this history of American railroads.

*Rocket Away!* by Frances Frost.

David and Jean go to the Planetarium and make a rocket trip to the moon.

# They Worked to Win

# Magic Money

## *Tony's Secret*

Tony had a secret. It was not a secret not-to-tell. It was a secret wanting that was most important. From the very first day that he had wanted this something, it had been big. It lived with Tony every day because he kept thinking about it. At night he dreamed about it.

The something Tony wanted was for his grandfather. Only a short time ago his grandfather's second ox had died. He had no money to buy another. So he was no longer able to work at the great plantation. He was too old to work in the fields, and now that his oxen were gone, he could do nothing at all.

Tony wanted to earn some money to buy another team of oxen for his grandfather. This was his secret. It was a very big secret.

Tony lived in Costa Rica. There were trees and flowers and tall grasses around the little house in which he lived with his father and mother, and his big brother Roberto. His grandfather had a little house of his own, up the road from Tony's house.

172

On the morning that this story begins, Tony was
standing at the door of the house watching the rain.
The rain came every morning. It was a warm rain
and made bananas ripen and sugar cane grow.

His mother was washing the breakfast dishes.
She saw Tony standing in the door watching the
rain. She knew something was troubling him.
She came to stand beside him and put a wet hand
on his shoulder.

"You have a secret, my Tony?"

"Yes, Mama, a secret."

"Can you tell me?"

"No, Mama, not until I am ready to get it."

"You will get it, Tony. I feel it in my heart. You will get your secret someday."

This made Tony feel better, but not much better. He knew he would need money to make his secret come true. He was nine years old. There are not many ways a boy of nine can earn money in Costa Rica, or any place, for that matter.

Tony's father and mother worked on the plantation picking coffee beans. It was so very large that many crops grew on it, but mostly the crops were sugar cane and coffee.

One day Tony asked his father for a job picking coffee beans at the big plantation.

"That is very hard work for a small boy," his father told him.

But Tony wanted to try. The basket he carried was almost as tall as he was. The branches where the coffee beans grew were high over his head. He had to reach very far to pull them down to him.

His arms ached and his shoulders began to hurt. Tony sat down in the shade of a tree and rested his head against the coffee basket. He went to sleep and did not awaken until Mama called him at lunchtime. He had earned no money at all!

One other day Tony said to himself, "I will tell Grandfather a little about my secret. Grandfather can help me, I know it."

Grandfather lived alone and did his own housework. His house was very clean. Now Tony came up on the wide porch in front of the house. He saw his grandfather's high woodpile on one side. The beautiful painted ox-cart stood in the yard near the porch. But the ox-cart could not take the cane to the mill where the brown sugar was made. Grandfather had no oxen left to pull it.

175

"Good morning," Grandfather said when Tony came into the house. "It is good to see you."

"Grandfather," Tony began, "I have a secret."

"A secret, lad? A secret must not be told."

"No, Grandfather, but I need to earn some money to buy it, and there is no way I can earn money," said Tony. "I have tried. The work in the coffee plantation is too hard. There is nothing else."

Grandfather thought a minute. "If you cannot do something to earn money, then you must make something."

Tony's eyes lighted. "What should I make?" he asked.

Grandfather got up. "Come," he said, and Tony followed him outside. He pointed to the ox-cart.

"See that ox-cart standing over there, Tony?"

"Yes, Grandfather."

"Close your eyes, young fellow. Can't you see it going down the road, proud in its lovely painted beauty? Can't you see it being pulled by two great oxen?"

"Yes, oh, yes!"

"Of course you can! Oxen and the cart they pull are a country man's riches. To young and old they mean one thing. They mean a proud possession. Men have this great possession at least once in their lifetime. But children? Children never have it while they are children. So we will give the children oxen and an ox-cart while they are young. It will be their own possession to love, to care for, and to play with. We will make it small but perfect. We will make it out of wood."

"A toy, Grandfather? A toy ox-cart and oxen for some small boy to play with? Can we make it now?" Tony began to dance excitedly.

"Now! Today!" said Grandfather. "Come, we will go for wood."

Day after day Tony and his grandfather worked at making the toy. They kept it a secret from everyone.

## The Secret Is Out

At last the day came when the cart and oxen were finished. Two little oxen and a perfect little cart! Everything was perfect.

Tony and his grandfather carried them carefully down the road to Tony's house. His father and mother and Roberto could hardly believe their eyes. The little cart looked just like the one in grandfather's yard. Only Tony had made his own designs for the toy cart. Each one of the four sides had a different design. It was green and yellow and red and white.

"Tomorrow," said Tony's mother, "we will go to market, and Tony will try to sell his cart and oxen."

Grandfather did not like to go to the market. It was too crowded in the city, he said. The houses with their red roofs and iron balconies were too close together. There were too many people about. So Tony and Roberto and their father and mother got aboard the bus and went bumping and rattling along the road to the city. Tony held his cart and oxen very carefully across his knees.

The bus stopped at the edge of the market. Tony had never seen so many people walking around the square. There were people everywhere, and everywhere people were trying to sell something. People from the city were walking along, glancing about, and deciding what to buy.

Tony and his family walked along. Tony held out the ox-cart so that the people coming to buy could get a good look at it.

Suddenly he saw two ladies walking toward them. They were not Costa Rican ladies. They wore flat-heeled shoes, not high-heeled pointed slippers like the rich ladies of Costa Rica. They wore hats. The ladies stopped. One of them had blue eyes. She pointed to Tony's cart. She spoke to him in Spanish. Her Spanish sounded funny. "She is from North America," Tony's mother said.

"I would like to buy your cart and oxen," the lady said in Spanish to Tony. "How much are you asking for it?"

180

Tony had not thought about how much he would ask for his cart. He couldn't say one word.

His father spoke now. "I think Tony would be pleased with whatever you think the cart is worth."

The blue-eyed lady handed Tony six colones. Six colones!

"Thank you, thank you," Tony said, and handed her the cart.

A wave of joy washed over him. Six colones! Money! His dream had come true. Now he could buy what he had dreamed of buying. He had money at last!

"What are you buying with your money, Tony?"

All the family looked at him. Tony held the coins tighter.

"Is it still a secret?" his father asked him.

"It is something for Grandfather," was all Tony would say.

It was late when they went to find the bus to take them home. When they got off at their stop, Tony ran down the road to Grandfather's house.

The old man was sitting at his supper table. He was eating rice and beans and drinking coffee. When Tony came into the room, he pushed his plate and cup away. He looked at Tony.

Tony's cheeks were red and his eyes were shining. "Grandfather! A lady bought it! A lady bought the cart and oxen. She gave me money. I have it. I did not spend it."

Grandfather made Tony sit down. He listened while Tony told all that had happened—everything. Now there was only one thing left to tell.

"This is the money," Tony said, holding out his hand toward his Grandfather. "This is for you, my Grandfather. This money—it is for you to buy two great white oxen. Two great white oxen, Grandfather, to pull your cart again to the sugarcane mill."

"Tony!" Grandfather said. "Tony! Tony! You did this for me?"

182

Grandfather looked at the money. How could he tell Tony that six colones could not buy oxen? It was not enough, not enough by a hundred times. How could he tell him? Tony knew money only as money. There had never been enough in his small world to know that it takes big money to buy big things.

Tony was talking. "Tomorrow, Grandfather, you can go tomorrow to buy your two white oxen."

"Tony, Tony! Money is not just money, my little boy. It first must be how big, how many, and then, how much. Six colones are not enough to buy two white oxen."

"Not enough, Grandfather? Not enough? Not big enough?" Tony looked puzzled.

Grandfather shook his head.

"Can't money do everything, Grandfather? Isn't money magic? People are always saying, 'Money is magic.' Isn't money really magic, Grandfather?"

Again Grandfather shook his head.

"Money is not magic," he began and then something seemed to happen to him. He seemed taller. He seemed younger. His voice was strong, not broken now. It was almost like a song.

183

"Tony—" Even the shadows in the room stood still, listening. "Tony, money can be magic. It is what it makes you do. Yes. Yes. Money can be magic. Good magic. See what it has done to me? You saw me old, but now I am not old. I am young. My thinking and my heart are young again. I will not sit here crying because I can no longer lead the others in the cane field. No! I will work again. You and I will be partners in a business. We will make toy oxen and toy ox-carts painted in beautiful designs. We will sell them at the market. We will save the money."

Grandfather took the six colones. He found a can to put them in. "When this can is full, my Tony, you and I will buy our oxen, our two great white oxen."

184

"Our oxen, Grandfather?"

"Our oxen, Tony. Soon, too, I know it. My heart tells me it will be soon. Every Saturday we will go to market with our toy oxen to sell. Yes, Tony, maybe we will have two, three, four to sell. Who knows how many? Who knows how much money they will bring?"

"Oh, Grandfather, money is magic!"

"Money can be magic."

A knock came at the door. It was Tony's father with his lantern.

"Tomorrow," Grandfather told him, "tomorrow we will tell you about our business, but tonight"— Grandfather's voice softened— "tonight a tired boy must sleep."

"Tony's eyes asked, "Tomorrow?"

Grandfather's eyes promised, "Tomorrow."

Tony's father said, "Come. I have brought my lantern to light you safely home."

Grandfather stood at his door and watched Tony and his father go down the ribbon of road to Tony's house.

*Ann Nolan Clark*

185

# Just Enough

## Sarah's Idea

The harvest was almost over. It made Sarah feel somehow rather sad, for the harvest had been fun. She and her younger sister were walking through the lonely prune orchard.

The two girls stopped and looked upon the cold campfire where the prune-pickers had cooked their food. A few dry leaves lay scattered on the ground. Sarah kicked at them and saw three prunes roll ahead of her foot.

186

"Those prunes won't do anyone any good now." Linda sounded quite troubled.

"I wonder if Father knows about it," Sarah said. "Maybe he hadn't noticed that they haven't all dropped off the trees yet. There goes one now."

As she spoke, a fat ripe prune fell at her feet.

Linda looked up excitedly. "Let's tell him," she said.

Glad of something interesting to do, the girls ran toward the drying field, where Father and Joe were piling trays of prunes.

"Father!" Linda began calling the second he came from behind a pile of prune trays. "Father, there are still some prunes left in the orchard. Shouldn't they be picked?"

Father helped Joe swing a tray of prunes into place before he turned to smile at Linda.

"I know," he said. "It does seem too bad. But you see, so few prunes are left that it wouldn't pay any men to pick them. They wouldn't make enough to pay for their time. There wouldn't be over ten boxes of fruit on the twenty acres."

"But isn't it good?" Sarah asked anxiously.

"As good as any in the crop that we have harvested," he answered.

Suddenly an idea popped into Sarah's mind. Her heart began to thump loudly. It was such a splendid idea! If only Father would say yes to it! She tried to speak, but her mouth was all at once so dry that it couldn't make words. At last she swallowed hard and spoke in a strange voice, not at all like her own.

"Father!"

"What is it, Sarah?" Father was bending over a tray of prunes.

"Father," Sarah began. She wished Joe and Linda weren't there. She was afraid they might laugh at her. The idea seemed silly now that she was about to put it into words.

"Well, Sarah?" Father was looking at her in a questioning way.

"Father, may I have the prunes that are left? I mean" —Sarah rushed on— "I mean, if I pick them up, may I have the money they will bring?"

Father laughed and turned back to his work.

"It's quite a job, Sarah. You'd have to cover the whole orchard."

"I know," said Sarah. "But please let me."

She sounded as if she just had to do it, as if it were very important somehow.

Father straightened up to look at his daughter. He saw her dark eyes gazing hard at him, while she waited anxiously for his answer.

"All right," Father said slowly. "But unless you cover the whole orchard, I can't take the trouble to fire the lye pot and dip the prunes. All or nothing! Is it agreed?"

"Oh, yes," Sarah breathed happily. "And thank you, Father."

189

## Sarah's Helper

Sarah was so excited she hardly knew what to do now that her wish seemed to be coming true. Instead of hurrying off to pick prunes as fast as possible, she appeared to be rooted to the ground.

Only one thought was perfectly clear to her. If she picked ten boxes of prunes, she could sell them, and with the money she could buy a burro. A little gray burro with brown markings over its shoulders! At last she could have the burro she had wanted for such a very long time.

She felt as if she must shout her good luck to all the world. But she held her tongue. It was better to keep her secret until she had the money.

And then, right in the middle of her happy thoughts, she heard Linda saying, "I'll help you, Sarah. You'll get through much quicker if I help."

Sarah could hardly believe her ears. Think of Linda offering to pick prunes! Linda, who didn't like dirt, was saying that she wanted to crawl over twenty acres of it!

That was surprising. But it would mean, too, the end of Sarah's wish. For if Linda helped to pick the prunes, she would want half the money they brought. And Sarah was sure it would take every dime that ten boxes would bring to buy a burro.

"What's the matter, Sarah? Don't you want me to help you?" asked Linda.

Sarah looked at her sister and was surprised to see that Linda's eyes were full of tears. Whatever was the matter?

"Don't you want me to help you?" she asked again in a tight little voice.

Sarah cleared her throat. "Yes, of course, Linda. Only I want the money for something very important. I—I need all the prunes myself."

She knew it sounded selfish and was glad Father and Joe had moved out of hearing.

Sarah really felt sorry for Linda, but Linda no longer seemed to feel sorry about anything. All her tears had gone. She was even smiling as happily as if something splendid had happened to her.

"Oh, I don't want any money, Sarah. I just want to help you. Truly!"

Sarah looked into Linda's clear eyes raised to hers, and suddenly she felt selfish and small. In that second she knew that as long as she lived, she would never be as unselfish and fine as Linda, no matter how hard she tried.

But there was nothing to stop her trying. She would start right away, not by giving Linda half the money, but by making Linda a partner in the secret. They would buy a burro together. Why hadn't she thought of it before?

"I'll be very glad if you'll help, Linda," said Sarah.

"Shall we start right now?" Linda believed in never putting off anything.

"Let's," agreed Sarah, feeling as if a heavy lump of loneliness had been lifted from her heart.

192

# Partners at Work

Eager and excited, each girl took a row of trees. They started at the very back of the orchard, deciding that it would be more fun to work toward the house than away from it.

"We can play we're going to find the Promised Land," said Sarah. "The house and barn will be the Promised Land."

"And the prune picking will be the troubles we go through," agreed Linda from the next row. Her face was quite red, but she was bravely keeping up with Sarah. Both girls were making the leaves fly as they shook each tree for whatever fruit might still be hanging to its branches.

"Sarah, what are you going to do with the money when you get it?" asked Linda, stopping a minute to rest.

Sarah had been waiting for this question, and had kept the secret until the question should be asked. It made it easier.

"That's what I want to tell you," she said, crossing over from her row of trees to join Linda. "As long as you want to help, I've decided to let you be a partner with me. We're going to buy a burro."

Linda's blue eyes grew round. "Truly?" she asked.

Sarah nodded.

"Did Father say yes?" questioned Linda.

"I haven't asked him," Sarah had to say.

"But maybe he won't let us have a burro." Linda put into words the very thing that Sarah just wouldn't believe. It was the thing her mind had kept turning away from.

"I'm sure he would if we had the money to buy one," Sarah said.

She was trying to believe so herself as much as to make Linda believe so. Their secret wish had to come true.

194

"Well, anyway," said Linda, "let's ask him. Then if he won't let us, we can plan to do something else with the money. It's more fun working if you know what you are working for. I do hope he'll let us have the burro, though. You know, Sarah, I think that's the best idea you've ever had."

Sarah thought so, too, but she kept from saying so. It was agreed that they would ask Father at noon when they went up to the house for lunch.

All morning Sarah felt a heavy lump in her stomach, and her throat tightened every time she thought of Father's saying no. The prunes would mean nothing if they couldn't buy her a burro.

But that noon when they told the plan to Father, he looked at them for a long minute. Then he said, in a pleased voice, that if two little girls wanted a burro badly enough to pick prunes for it, they should have one.

For the next week Sarah and Linda spent most of their time in the orchard picking their prunes. Linda was a splendid picker. One might almost have thought she really liked the work.

But Linda believed in doing a job as quickly as possible and being done with it. Because she was willing to pick prunes didn't mean she liked it.

At last one day they came in sight of the Promised Land. Looking down the rows of trees, they could just see the red wall of the barn.

After that it seemed no time at all before the picking was finished, and twelve boxes of prunes stood on the dipping platform. Sarah and Linda gazed proudly on their work. They had harvested more prunes than Father had thought possible.

Father was building a fire under the tank full of lye and water into which the prunes would be dipped. Without this dipping, they would spoil.

"How long before the water will be hot?" questioned Linda.

"A few hours," Father answered. "Do you think you girls can feed the firebox while I go back to the drying field to help Joe?"

196

"Oh, yes," they both said at once.

Later, when the last prunes had been dipped into the lye pot, Father and Joe moved the trays of wet fruit. They took them from the dipping platform to the drying field and left the prunes there to dry in the hot sun.

"That's a fine lot of prunes," Father told the girls, "and I'm proud to think you harvested them all yourselves."

That made Sarah and Linda feel proud.

"Do you think they will bring enough dollars to buy a burro?" Linda asked.

Father thought for a minute, while the sisters watched him anxiously.

"You know, I believe they will," he said at last with a nod. "Yes, I'm almost sure that they'll bring just enough to buy a burro."

He sounded very sure, and even Joe, standing near, smiled at the good news.

That evening Sarah gave the empty stall in the red barn a good sweeping. She had been keeping it ready for this very day. She swept the floor with the old barn broom until her arms ached. She made the job last as long as she possibly could.

When she was done, she stood for a long while gazing into the stall. And clearer than ever before she could see a burro standing there.

A gray burro—a small gray burro with brown markings over its shoulders!

*Doris Gates*

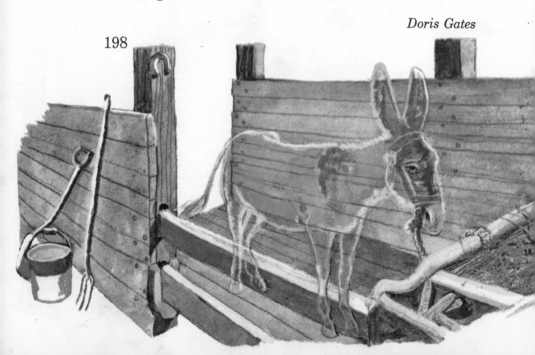

# Old Tom

When Malcolm was young, he lived with his father and mother and his Aunt Sue in a small house in the middle of the pine woods. On each side the land sloped down to a river. A road ran by through the forest. Toward the east it led at last to farms, a bridge, and the town and railroad eight miles away. Toward the west it wandered off into the hills and back country.

For a time the family had no neighbors, and Malcolm made up his own games in the woods which lay all about his house. He had a great love for special trees, and he knew every path and clearing. He never met anyone in his wanderings until Old Tom came to live in the empty cabin halfway down to the south branch of the river.

199

"He's a good man but grouchy," Malcolm's father explained. "Last winter a tree fell on him and broke his leg badly. Now he's too lame to work any more. He's worked for us a good many years, and I thought we should look after him. I told him he could use the cabin as long as he liked."

"It will be good to have a neighbor," said Aunt Sue, but Father laughed.

"You won't find grouchy Old Tom much of a neighbor," he said. "Just leave him alone to go his own way."

The first that Malcolm knew was that one morning he saw a little smoke from a chimney blowing off along the tops of the pines. He guessed Old Tom had come. So he took the narrow path rough with great rocks and pine roots, and came to the cabin. It was even more deeply hidden in the woods than his own house.

The door stood open, and as Malcolm watched, a broom-end appeared sweeping dust and dirt through the doorway. Next appeared the sweeper, an older man who moved slowly with a limp, his heavy boots making an uneven clumping sound. He had shaggy eyebrows which didn't spoil his eyesight, for he saw Malcolm at his first glance.

"Hi!" he shouted. "You get out of here, quick!" That was Malcolm's first meeting with Old Tom.

When two people use the same woods as much as Malcolm and Old Tom did, they are sure to meet often. Malcolm sometimes came upon the man face to face on some path, or fishing from the bank of the river. Sometimes he heard him chopping down a tree for firewood. Once in a while he met him limping along with his gun, with a squirrel or rabbit hung over his shoulder for a stew.

Malcolm always spoke to the woodsman politely, and after the first meeting, the man would answer with a grouchy hello under his breath as they passed on the narrow woodland path.

When Malcolm's mother went to town, she brought back a few supplies for Old Tom, one week beans, another tea and vinegar and salt, again, some flour and molasses. Malcolm was sent to take them to the cabin. He left them at the doorstep, gave one knock, and hurried off without looking behind him as he heard the door open.

Once he thought that Old Tom called, "Thanks," after him, but he wasn't sure. Then one day Malcolm found Old Tom starting to cut off the branch of his favorite beech tree, the branch he used as a stairway when he climbed.

The beech tree was old, and its branches spread out very wide, one of them touching the side of the hill so that Malcolm could walk along it right into the heart of the tree.

That day Malcolm was carrying the top of a wooden box to make another platform high in the tree. When he heard the hollow sound of an ax coming from the direction of the beech, he started to run. He arrived breathless and caught at the woodcutter's arm.

"Oh, please don't, Mr. Tom," he begged. "That's the way I go up."

Old Tom stared at him crossly.

"Your pa said I could cut anything I'd a mind to," he answered.

"Pa didn't remember my trees," said Malcolm, trying hard to be polite and patient. "I have ten of them and they each have a name. This is Big Gray and the best of them all. If you cut off that branch, I can't ever climb it again."

203

He stood looking anxiously into Old Tom's face. At last Old Tom gave a kind of grunt and limped off. After twenty steps he turned back. His eyes looked more kindly under their shaggy brows.

"You'd best mark the rest of your trees, boy, or I'm likely to take a swing at them someday."

Then he nodded and made off again.

About a week later something happened which surprised Malcolm. There was a small pond—Malcolm called it Round Pond—in a hollow of the woods. It wasn't more than six or seven feet across and three feet deep, but it never dried up.

Malcolm used to go there on hot days, and this morning he found a little birch-bark canoe in the middle of Round Pond. It was an exact copy of a real Indian canoe, curved at bow and stern, and there was a little paddle in it. On the sand at the edge of the pond Malcolm found the other paddle and a mark as though the birch-bark canoe had been pushed out into the water.

For the next two days it rained, but when good weather came again, Malcolm hurried down to Round Pond. The birch-bark canoe was still there.

A day or two later he went to Big Gray. As he walked along his branch stairway, he saw a squirrel staring down at him through the leaves, but the creature didn't scold and scamper away as Malcolm came near. It stayed right where it was, and when he looked closer, he saw that the squirrel had been carved from white pine.

Things grew more and more exciting. Malcolm could hardly sit through his breakfasts, he was so anxious to get out into the woods.

One day he came upon a little carved bear cub on a moss-covered log. Another day there was a wooden mouse in a small cave which he thought no one else knew about. He found a very thin big-eared owl on a branch of another of his trees.

205

Once a tiny pine-wood sleigh stood beside the path. Again some white stones led him to an old carton in which he discovered writing paper and envelopes made from birch bark.

Malcolm was never lonely any more.

Could his playfellow be Old Tom? Yet the woodcutter seemed as gruff as ever when they met on the paths or the boy left groceries at the cabin door. One week there was a letter with the groceries, and a few days later Malcolm came on Old Tom carrying a small traveling bag, and walking toward town and the railroad.

"Oh, you're not going away, Mr. Tom?" he cried out before he had time to think, and for once Old Tom gave him a real answer.

"No, boy. Back Thursday," he explained and then scowled as though he'd talked too much.

Back Thursday! Fall was coming on, and Old Tom wouldn't be home until nearly dark if he came on the three o'clock train from Boston. The cabin would be cold, and there would be no one to welcome him.

On Thursday, as Malcolm played in the woods, he glanced at the cabin. How he wished he could make it cheerful for Old Tom's return.

But did Malcolm dare to pull out the stick which fastened the door and go right into the cabin? Would Old Tom be angry and chase him up the path? Malcolm's mouth pressed into a straight line, and he opened the door and went in.

All afternoon he worked around the cabin. It was very clean, but he brought in dry firewood and a bucket of spring water. He laid a fire in the iron stove, sweeping up with the broom any dust he had made. At last he put the broom away and went back to the house.

Then he asked his Aunt Sue, who was cook that week, for some bread-and-cheese sandwiches and his lunch pail full of stew and for what was left of the apple pie.

"Going to take your supper out?" she asked.

Malcolm nodded. He often camped out all day in the woods, and his family didn't mind. So Aunt Sue said, "Yes," as he had hoped, and got the picnic lunch ready.

"May I have another sandwich, please, and a little more stew?" he asked.

"My, you're hungry this afternoon," said Aunt Sue, dishing into the pail big spoonfuls of the meat, turnips, and potatoes, and cutting more bread.

Then he went down the path to Old Tom's place. It looked nice in the late afternoon sunlight. Now he lighted the stove, put out the sandwiches, and laid two places. He found only one bowl for the stew but put a cup at the other place. After he cut the pie in two pieces, Malcolm went to the door and looked out.

The sun was now in the tops of the trees, and soon only the sea gull far overhead caught the sunlight on outstretched wings.

Malcolm shut the door, lighted the tallow candle in its saucer, and waited. Hours seemed to pass, and then at last he heard the uneven tramping of Old Tom's boots coming down the path. Malcolm got up in sudden fright, but it was too late.

208

The door opened, and there stood Old Tom, filling the narrow doorway. The cold came in with him. His bright blue eyes under their shaggy brows stared about the room, at the warm stove, the pail of stew, and the dishes laid out ready on the table. Then he looked at Malcolm.

"Boy," he said, "I feel more at home than I have for thirty years," and instead of saying, "Thank you," or anything like that, he just sniffed the air and asked, as he put down his bag, "Do I smell stew?"

When Malcolm said, "Yes," Old Tom growled, "Well, wash up, I'm hungry as a bear."

They gave their hands a lick and a promise at the washbowl on the box beside the door. Then they sat down together like two old friends and began their supper.

*Elizabeth Coatsworth*

## Lincoln

There was a boy of other days,
A quiet, awkward, earnest lad,
Who trudged long weary miles to get
A book on which his heart was set—
And then no candle had!

He was too poor to buy a lamp,
But very wise in woodmen's ways.
He gathered seasoned bough and stem,
And crisping leaf, and kindled them
Into a ruddy blaze.

Then as he lay full length and read,
The firelight flickered on his face,
And etched his shadow on the gloom,
And made a picture in the room,
In that most humble place.

The hard years came, the hard years went,
But gentle, brave, and strong of will,
He met them all.  And when today
We see his pictured face, we say,
"There's light upon it still."

*Nancy Byrd Turner*

# Dogs and Weather

I'd like a different kind of dog
  For every kind of weather—
A narrow greyhound for a fog,
  A wolfhound strange and white,
With a tail like a silver feather
  To run with in the night,
When snow is still and winter stars are bright.

In the fall I'd like to see
  In answer to my whistle,
A golden spaniel look at me.
  But best of all for rain
A terrier, hairy as a thistle,
  To trot with fine disdain
Beside me down the soaked, sweet-smelling lane.

*Winifred Welles*

212

# The Seventh Pup

## Not Wanted

In some ways Billy Bent was a very lucky boy, and he knew it. In other ways he wasn't lucky.

In the first place Billy loved dogs. He had decided that when he grew up he was going to earn his living by training them. That wouldn't happen for quite a while, though, because Billy was only nine years old. But he had a way with dogs and an eye for them too.

Anyway, that's what his neighbor Mr. Riggs said, and he should have known, for he raised Boston terriers. People for miles around came to buy them.

The people Billy lived with next door were paid by the city to take care of him, because he had no family. That was not lucky, but living next door to Mr. Riggs was lucky.

Now one day Queenie, the best dog Mr. Riggs owned, had a litter of puppies. Billy happened to be right there when Mr. Riggs found Queenie's new family.

"Well, old lady," Mr. Riggs said gently, and Queenie looked at him with clear, unafraid eyes. "How many babies have you this time?"

He moved Queenie to one side and found seven black-and-white puppies. Mr. Riggs was very much pleased, for buyers always wanted Queenie's puppies. She was one of the best Boston terriers in the world.

All these new-born puppies had strong bodies and perfect markings. All but one! His markings were anything but perfect. His white shirt front came too far around his shoulders like a shawl. One half of his face was black and the other, white. On the white side he had a black ear, and on the black side, a white ear.

He couldn't have looked more sadly mixed up, but saddest of all was his tail. It was two times as long as it should have been.

"Well," said Mr. Riggs, "it won't be hard to decide what to do with that seventh pup." He had put the six good puppies in the box, and the seventh was all by himself on the floor.

"What do you mean?" asked Billy, but in his heart he knew what Mr. Riggs was going to say.

"Queenie won't have milk for more than six puppies, and that seventh one isn't any good anyway. I'll just have to kill him."

Billy looked at the seventh pup, and all at once he knew that he loved him better than all the rest of Queenie's litter put together. Maybe it was because the puppy wasn't wanted.

Billy knew that feeling of not being wanted, because nobody cared much about him, either.

215

Maybe the puppy felt the same way. So now Billy wanted that homely seventh pup. He wanted him more than anything in all the world.

"Yes, I'll have to kill him," Mr. Riggs said, "but he's so homely, it won't matter much."

Then Billy spoke. "Don't kill him," he begged. "Give him to me."

Mr. Riggs looked at Billy in surprise. "He's too little to take away from his mother," he said. "You couldn't feed him, boy."

"Yes, I could," Billy said eagerly. "I'll feed him with a baby's bottle. And if he doesn't keep well and strong—why then I'll give him up."

Mr. Riggs could think of nothing to say against Billy's plan, and so he gave him the pup and one of the baby bottles which he kept at the kennel. Then Billy went proudly home with the seventh pup held close in his arms. This was his first dog.

The man who was paid for keeping Billy was working in the yard when Billy reached the house.

"Where on earth did you find that?" he scolded.

Billy tried to smile as he asked anxiously, "How do you like my dog?"

"What do you mean by 'my dog'?" The man's voice was sharp.

"Mr. Riggs just gave him to me for keeps."

"Well, you can take him right back," said the man. "What made you think you could have a dog? Besides, he's about the homeliest thing I ever had to look at."

"I'll keep him in the basement or under the back porch and take care of him. He won't be in anybody's way," said Billy.

"That's easy to say," said the man. "You take him right back to Mr. Riggs."

# A Job for Billy

Billy had to obey. He walked sadly back to the kennel with the pup, but Mr. Riggs wouldn't take him back.

"He's your dog," he told Billy, who was trying to rub the tears off his face. "When I give a dog, I give him for good."

"But he"—Billy nodded toward the house next door—"he won't let me keep him."

"How about keeping him over here?" suggested Mr. Riggs.

"I haven't any money to pay for his keep," said Billy, without any hope.

"I haven't asked for money," said Mr. Riggs, and smiled. "I thought maybe you'd like to earn the pup's keep."

Billy gave a huge sniff and looked with surprised eyes at Mr. Riggs. "How?" he asked.

"I've seen for some time that you have a way with dogs," Mr. Riggs said. "I'll need a little help, now that this new litter has arrived. Suppose you come over whenever you get the chance and mix feed and clean kennels, and I'll board the pup for your pay."

218

Billy's face broke into a smile so bright that Mr. Riggs couldn't face it and had to look down at the ground for a minute. Billy could hardly believe what he'd heard. Work for the pup's board! Why, he'd rather be working around dogs than doing anything else in the world.

"Thanks, Mr. Riggs," he said. "Thanks!"

The puppy wiggled and tried to wag his tail. Mr. Riggs laughed. "His tail isn't too long to wag, even if it is too long for a terrier."

Soon Billy and Mr. Riggs began calling the seventh pup Too-long because of his too-long tail.

The weeks passed and then the months. Too-long grew, and his tail grew with him.

From the first he got along wonderfully on Billy's care. Most likely that was because there was so much love mixed up in it.

After all, it turned out to be a lucky thing that the people Billy lived with didn't care much about him. If they had, they might not have wanted him to spend so much time away from home.

As it was, Billy spent more time at the Riggs place than he did at his own. As soon as school was over, he ran next door, where Too-long fell upon him with sharp barks of welcome.

219

Billy was careful not to spoil him. And whenever he had a chance, he worked with the pup, teaching him the things a well-trained dog should know. By the time Too-long was six months old, he had learned to follow close at Billy's heels, to lie down when told to do so, and to bring a ball right to his master's feet. He obeyed each command with such an eager wag of his tail that teaching him was fun.

Even Mr. Riggs said that Too-long, for all his homeliness, was as smart as a whip and not a bit spoiled. By the time he was a year old and Billy was ten, Too-long stayed exactly where he was told to stay, jumped over a stick to bring the ball, spoke, shook hands, and rolled over. Billy thought he was the most wonderful dog in the world.

220

"You've done a good job with him," Mr. Riggs said. "You like him so much, I was afraid you'd spoil him. It's too bad he can't ever go into the show ring. He could be a winner with what he knows if he just had looks to go along with it."

## The Dog Show

Then, one day just a month before the dog show, bad luck decided to pay a visit to Mr. Riggs. The only dog he had planned to show that year was taken sick. Mr. Riggs's face looked as long as Too-long's tail.

Billy, seeing how sad Mr. Riggs looked, began to think hard. He knew Too-long's papers were all in order. Mr. Riggs had seen to that. So one day Billy went to see the man who was head of the town's kennel club. He told Billy what to do and helped him.

Billy didn't say a word about his plan to Mr. Riggs, but the evening before the show day he gave Too-long a bath and brushed him carefully.

The next morning Billy put a collar and a rope on Too-long. With the little dog at his heels he started for the dog show.

Two hours later Mr. Riggs, walking about and looking at the barking dogs, came at last to the ring where a large crowd had gathered. The obedience trials for boy and girl trainers were being held there. Mr. Riggs stopped to watch, but at first he could not see what was going on. When at last he got a good look, his mouth opened wide in surprise.

There, jumping bars and going through his tricks as easily and perfectly as he did in his own back yard, was Too-long. And with him was Billy, the boy nobody cared very much about.

Mr. Riggs remembered then that there is one part of every dog show where looks don't count. That part is the obedience trials. If a dog has papers, is in good condition, and does exactly what his master commands him to do, nobody cares what he looks like. And if he obeys perfectly enough, he can even win a blue ribbon.

222

Mr. Riggs felt his eyes grow wet as he watched the little dog, with his tail held out straight and long behind him. There was such an eagerness in the way he tried to obey Billy's commands that it seemed as if he knew he was the only dog from his kennel who had a chance of bringing home a prize ribbon that day.

Billy was as eager as the dog. His face was red and anxious, and he never once looked at the crowd.

He didn't seem to hear the cheers when Too-long jumped the low bars and brought him the dumb-bell. He was busy trying to send thought messages to Too-long that the bars were just the stick at home, and the dumbbell only a ball.

Too-long did everything Billy told him to. And he carried the dumbbell so proudly that he seemed to be saying thanks to the people for watching him. The homely little dog had won the hearts of the people.

At last it was over, and a man came up to Billy and handed him a blue ribbon. Too-long had won first place in the obedience trials for boy and girl trainers.

224

Mr. Riggs caught up with Billy outside. "I saw you in there," he said. "I was proud of you."

Billy held out the blue ribbon that Too-long had just won. "You can put it in the glass box with the others," he said. "The kennel will have a ribbon to show for this year after all."

Mr. Riggs took the ribbon. "Thank you, Billy," he said. "I'm very happy about what you've done for the kennel. And there's another thing. I think after what happened today that Too-long has earned his own keep. How would it seem to work for real money instead of for his board?"

"For you?" asked Billy, a light coming into his face and expressing his thanks better than words.

"For me," said Mr. Riggs, "outside school hours."

Billy grinned. "I'd like it a lot."

"Then you're to be my right-hand man," said Mr. Riggs, and rested his hand on Billy's shoulder. Under it he could feel Billy pull his shoulders up very straight.

*Doris Gates*

225

# Things to Think About and Do

1. The settings for all the stories and poems in this unit are somewhere in America. See how many clues you can find that tell you where each character lived. If you have to guess about any story or poem, be able to give a good reason for your guess. Make a list of all the clues you find for each story.

2. On an outline map of America show where each story or poem may have taken place. Then on the part of the map where you think each leading character lived, write his or her name. If you decide to make a picture map, how will you show where each character lived?

3. Copy on a sheet of paper the sentences that tell ways in which Linda and Sarah were alike. Be ready to prove your point by reading a sentence from the story "Just Enough."

> They were unselfish.
> They liked to do a job well.
> They never put off anything.
> They were good workers.
> They wanted a burro.
> They had blue eyes.

4. Malcolm went into Old Tom's cabin without asking if he might do so. Why was he afraid that Old Tom would be angry? Why was Old Tom pleased to find Malcolm there? Is it ever right to go into other people's houses without being asked? Why or why not? Be ready to give two or three reasons for your answer.

5. Each word below has two or more meanings. You will find one meaning on the page listed with the word. Copy on a sheet of paper the sentence in which it is used. Now look the same word up in your glossary and write a new sentence using another meaning for the word.

anxious (page 187)    beam (page 87)
litter (page 214)     hull (page 160)
season (page 210)     stern (page 204)

6. Your group may divide into committees to set up displays about different kinds of dogs.

Make a list of the things you will do and then begin your share of the work on your committee.

7. Write a headline and newspaper story about Too-long and the prize he won. Tell how he won the prize, what it was, where and when it happened, and who owned the dog.

# Some Books to Read

*A Dog Named Penny*, by Clyde Robert Bulla.

A boy and girl care for a beautiful collie dog and earn her for their own.

*Jeb and the Flying Jenny,* by Dorothea Snow.

Jeb liked to whittle, and his hobby turned out to be very useful. He carved the wooden animals for a fly-around, the very first merry-go-round.

*Johnny of Johnnycake*, by Katharine Carter.

Johnny spent his time whittling and wishing until he found that it is better to work at making wishes come true.

*Magic Money*, by Ann Nolan Clark.

This is the book about Tony and his wonderful "wanting secret."

*Risky Business*, by Elaine Macmann.

When Terry goes into the turkey-raising business, he has to face and work out some amusing problems.

*Shoot for a Mule*, by Elisabeth Lansing.

This mountain boy knew what he wanted. What he wanted was a mule.

*Stars for Cristy*, by Mabel Leigh Hunt.

A city girl finds a way to make an unpromising summer turn out to be the best one ever.

# Here Come the Animals

# Seal Lullaby

Oh! hush thee, my baby, the night is behind us.
  And black are the waters that sparkled so
    green.
The moon, o'er the combers, looks downward to
    find us
  At rest in the hollows that rustle between.
Where billow meets billow, there soft be thy pillow;
  Ah, weary wee flipperling, curl at thy ease!
The storm shall not wake thee, nor shark overtake
    thee,
  Asleep in the arms of the slow-swinging seas.

*Rudyard Kipling*

# A Sea Family

Bobry was not a kitten, but his mother could hump her back like a cat, and hiss. She could even wash his soft fur with her tongue. Her face was whiskered like a cat's, too, and she loved to eat fish, as cats do. But she lived in the water most of the time and caught her own shellfish.

Bobry's mother used to hold him in her arms, almost as a human mother does her baby. She would lie on her back in the water and sing him to sleep with soft sounds.

Bobry's mother was really an otter. She had shining dark brown fur to keep her warm even when the sea was icy. The baby's fur was brown and shining, too.

Years ago there were a great number of otters in Bering Sea, where Bobry lived. But an otter's fur is so lovely that hunters caught many of them. Now those that still live have learned to hide when people are about.

Bobry was no larger than a squirrel. His father and mother were much larger than cats. Their bodies were long and ended in pointed tails. They could swim faster than anything else on four legs.

One of Bobry's early adventures was with a great horned owl. The mother otter had placed her baby on his back in the water to float. Then she went off to catch a shellfish for her own dinner.

Bobry floated about, sniffing the salt breeze. He held his paws over his eyes to keep out the light. Wide-winged sea birds circled above the waves looking for fish.

Soon a shadow fell across the water. It was the shadow of a bird with wings so softly feathered that it made no sound as it flew near. It was a great horned owl ready to swoop down upon Bobry.

Bobry was frightened by the dark shadow and began to cry. His crying sounded almost like that of a human baby.

Bobry's father was nearby, for he was always alert to danger. Otter babies are never left alone.

"Sssssss! Sssssss! SSSSSSS!" Father Otter hissed fiercely and humped up his back. Then he grabbed the baby otter in his mouth and dived deep into the water.

Before they reached the surface again, Mother Otter came swimming back like a shot. Rising half out of the water, she hissed fiercely at the great bird.

The hungry owl, seeing that he had missed his meal, flew away to hunt for other game.

One day a thick white fog rolled over the Bering Sea. Bobry could see nothing when his family swam to the shore for crabs.

Mother Otter loved crabs. She would break their shells on the stones. Then, taking the crab meat out of the shell with her paws, which she used like hands, she would wash it carefully until it was clear of sand. After eating, she would wash her face and paws like a cat.

Bobry and his mother were on their way home in the fog when an Eskimo boy, who had seen them one day from the high rock, passed in his boat. He had a fish net on the end of a pole. He threw the net over a fish and swung it into his boat. Then, as Bobry made a sound, the boy swung his net around and threw it over the little otter.

Quick as a flash Mother Otter made a dive. The next second Bobry felt her grab him in her mouth from under the water. He felt himself being pulled down, down, out of the net, and deep, deep into the sea. Water filled his eyes and nose, and he gave an angry cry.

Mother Otter had saved him from the net, but Bobry was too young to hold his breath for a long time under water. She had to bring him back to where he could breathe, or he would have drowned.

In the fog the Eskimo boy could not see them, but Bobry would not stay hidden. He was angry at his ducking. No sooner did he get his breath than he began to cry.

At that, the boy turned and paddled straight toward the sound, but he could see nothing. Not even a head was bobbing to the surface of the Bering Sea. Fog blanketed everything.

Again Mother Otter grabbed Bobry and dived under the waves with him. Had she been alone, it would have been easy for her to stay under water. Then the boy would not have known what had become of her, and soon would have gone away.

A second time she had to bring Bobry up for air. Once more the little fellow cried so loudly that the boy heard him.

This happened again and again. At last Mother Otter did what seemed like a very mean thing. She had to do it to save her baby's life. When Bobry opened his mouth to cry, she ducked him.

Bobry held fast to his mother, both paws around her neck. His crying was hushed only until she brought him up for air. Again she had to duck him, and again and again.

At last the little otter understood. Or if he didn't understand all about the boy and his net, he understood that he was not to cry.

So they hid in the thick fog until the boy gave
up trying to catch them and went away.

Bobry pressed his furry face deep into his
mother's neck, crying softly. Tears ran down his
small face, for otters cry real tears just as human
babies do. Mother Otter sheltered him in her arms
and licked his nose with her warm tongue, while
Father Otter swam close beside them.

Time passed, and Bobry was quite happy again.
He paddled in slow circles around his mother.
Anyone watching him would have thought he was
trying to tell her what a very clever young otter
her son would turn out to be someday!

*Allen Chaffee*

237

# The Snowshoe Rabbit Escapes

When the storm broke over the mountain forest, the young Snowshoe Rabbit was hiding under a clump of alders below the beaver pond. Crouched in a little hollow that she had dug in the snow, she looked only half her size.

She was tired. Beneath her warm body one of her feet ached and smarted. Three deep slashes throbbed with pain. The long furry foot that carried her so swiftly did not seem to belong to her at all.

If only she could close her eyes and sleep and sleep, more soundly than ever before! But she knew that was something a rabbit must never do. Even while she was sleeping, she must be on the alert. Her nose must always be smelling, sorting out the scents of the forest. Her ears must always be listening, even though they lay flat along her back out of sight.

238

She had so many enemies! The woods were full of them, and in winter they were hungrier than other times. Once they caught her scent, they never stopped tracking her down.

She tried not to move as she crouched there under the alders. Her safety lay in keeping still. The bobcat, the pine marten, the fox, the mountain lion, the coyote, the mink—all were on the lookout, always ready to track down a rabbit.

Without moving, she could see to the right and left at the same time. Now with one eye she was staring toward the beaver pond. That was where it had happened, there in the open space! That was where she had almost been caught.

The Snowshoe Rabbit stared at the open space. It had been the last danger spot for her to cross before reaching the clump of alders. She remembered the loud hoo-hoo that had started her heart to beating wildly. Something inside her had warned her to stand still, to freeze in her tracks. Something else had told her to escape, and she had fled just as a feathery shadow swooped down on her.

Somehow she had darted out of its clutch, but not without carrying away its mark. Claws had slashed into her foot as she leaped away. Before the hungry owl could swoop again, sharp claws ready to clutch her, she was safe beneath the alders.

It was beginning to snow. The heavy sky that pressed down over the valley was opening up and scattering starry flakes. The Snowshoe Rabbit felt safer now. Snowy branches above and around her would make a perfect shelter, for in winter she looked for all the world like a puff of snow.

The Snowshoe Rabbit stopped thinking about her narrow escape. She wiggled her nose and filled it with the wonderful smell of falling snowflakes. A deep snow would mean safety for her hide-out.

Let it snow long and hard. Tender alder buds and bark were close at hand. When night came, she could eat without moving more than a few feet from her white cave, and meanwhile take care of her foot and let it heal.

The day passed slowly. Nothing happened to frighten the furry mound of white crouched under the alders. Only the sky moved down, down, as the snowflakes covered last summer's spider webs and made the bushes blossom with winter flowers.

By evening the rabbit's foot seemed better. She licked it carefully and tenderly for a long time. Then to try it out, she hopped from her shelter into the deep fluff. Careful! Careful!

A few hops warned her not to go any farther. Her foot was throbbing again, smarting with pain. She would have little chance to escape from an enemy. The fierce, hungry owl could have easily swooped down and clutched her in his terrible claws if he had been near at this moment.

She reached up and nibbled at buds and bark above her head. For some minutes she ate, chewing quickly and wiggling her nose with delight. Then she hopped back into her shallow hole, out of sight in the shadows, and the first night of the storm passed.

Next morning it was still snowing. The Snowshoe Rabbit licked and tended her foot before daylight came with its frosty light. Her wounds were healing, slowly but surely.

Later in the day she woke from a nap with a start. All her senses were suddenly alert. She opened her ears wide. She took deep and careful sniffs. The scent of a mountain lion came to her on the snow!

242

Crouched into a little mound of white stillness, the Snowshoe Rabbit waited, alert to danger. Her heart thumped and her foot throbbed. She did not know how long it could carry her if she had to spring away.

She crouched, frightened, without moving or winking an eye. She would wait until the last moment before she fled.

Then the moment came. A cloud of snow, like a great puff of smoke, fell from one of the branches right behind her. She heard and saw it without turning. The lion was that close.

With a spring that stretched her body to its full length, the Snowshoe Rabbit leaped from her hidden shelter. Her body rounded together as her feet touched the snow, then stretched out full length again. With each spring she landed a good eight feet ahead.

The snow was packed enough to keep her from sinking down more than a few inches. She could make speed, for a little while at least, if only the sore foot would hold out!

She heard the lion rush after her, heard an angry hiss. Faster, faster the Snowshoe Rabbit's heart thumped, and faster her legs flew.

Suddenly everything was quiet behind her. The snow fell softly, and beneath every bush was a white cave just the right size to shelter a rabbit. Into one of these she leaped. Then, full of rabbity curiosity, she looked back. The lion was nowhere in sight.

The hurt foot, after carrying her so well, was full of pain again. The Snowshoe Rabbit hopped out of her hiding place and peered up the valley. She saw the mountain lion heading for the beaver house. She crouched down to rest. Little by little the excited beating of her heart slowed down. She felt very tired, eager to nap and forget her adventure with the lion.

244

Just as she was floating away on a rabbity cloud, like the down of a thistle, she saw something so terrible her strength flowed out of her. Her legs felt limp and helpless. A pine marten was coming toward her hide-out! The Snowshoe Rabbit knew, as the pine marten leaped ever closer, that she would have little chance to escape. His wide furred feet were almost as good as her snowshoes for carrying him over the snow.

Suddenly, from somewhere, her strength flowed back into her body. With a great burst of speed she was out of her hiding place and heading down the valley. She was running for her life.

A growl of anger came from behind her as the
marten followed. His leaps were much shorter
than hers, only two or three feet at a time, but
his speed was the kind that lasted. The Snowshoe
Rabbit knew in her heart that her foot could not
hold out for long. Yet she would not give up.
She would keep out of range of the marten as
long as there was breath in her body.

As she ran along the edge of the forest, another
brown body darted out toward her from the trees.
Another marten! Another racing enemy! What
chance had she now?

Then a fierce growl came from behind her. A
catlike hiss of anger followed it. Breathless, the
Snowshoe Rabbit darted into a clump of bushes
and stopped. Above the fast beating of her
heart she heard the two martens fighting fiercely.

They were fighting to the death. Terrible sounds came through the falling snow. She could hardly believe her luck. Now was her chance to escape.

Slipping around the bushes, she reached the long open lane of the frozen stream. There she leaped ahead. All of a sudden she turned and ran back in her tracks to some low bushes. With a mighty leap she jumped to the other side of the bushes and started ahead again.

If one of the martens followed her, he would have a hard time picking up her trail!

Very tired now, the Snowshoe Rabbit circled back to her home below the beaver pond. She crawled under another of her favorite bushes and became part of the snow.

The minutes passed as quietly as the falling snow. An hour went by. No marten came to hunt her out. She was safe in the snow.

*Aileen Fisher*

# The Captive Swans

## *The Trumpeters Arrive*

Kon—ng—kon—ng!

Clear as a trumpet the call came out of the sky. The air rang with the sound.

"What is it, Jean? What is it?" John cried fearfully.

Six-year-old John was a stranger in Canada. He was Jean's cousin and had come only last month to live with her family after his mother and father were killed in a plane wreck. Jean had always wanted a younger brother, and now here was John.

"Come, John," Jean said, taking him by the hand. "Let's be the first to see them."

"But what are they, Jean?" asked John, hanging back.

Jean laughed and explained, "They are birds, John. Beautiful, wonderful birds called swans. Trumpeter swans!"

Her words quieted the small boy's fears, and he let her lead him along the path to a spot where it touched the blue waters of the lake. The great white swans, wings shining in the sunlight, came down out of the cloudless sky into the water. More and more were coming with each second.

The birds closest to the shore arched their long necks, their black bills pointing toward the water. Now and then one of the trumpeters raised its wings in a shining arch behind it.

"They are very beautiful," said John. "Will they stay all summer?"

249

"Some of them will stay," Jean told him, "but the rest will move on. Every year two trumpeter swans have nested on the island out there. Swans are like us in the prairie lands. They build their homes away from their neighbors."

For several days Jean and John watched the swans resting and feeding on roots, seeds, and tiny water creatures. Then one day the great birds took wing. This year three pairs stayed behind. They could be seen every day flapping their great white wings, zooming into the air, and flying across the lake.

A few weeks later the three pairs of swans stopped their flights. Jean said to John, "The birds must be nesting. We will take the boat out to the island and see."

At the last minute Jean's father, Mr. Andrews, joined them. He worked the boat into a little inlet where two of the birds were feeding. At once they moved their long necks as if about to strike and began calling. John looked at them fearfully.

"Do not be afraid, John," Mr. Andrews said. "Swans in Canada may not be shot or hurt, and they seem to know that. Besides, this pair has nested here before. They know us as friends."

He pushed the boat farther into the inlet where they could get ashore. Then they climbed to higher ground.

In a little opening was the nest, a pile of rushes and sticks. As they came nearer, they saw a hollow in the top, lined with grass and down and feathers. There, warming in the sun, were six large, almost white eggs.

Mr. Andrews stopped. He picked up two of the eggs. "I think I'll take these," he said. "I heard a coyote the other night. He might get all the eggs. Maybe our hen can raise them."

"Oh, Daddy!" cried Jean. "One for John and one for me."

John looked pleased. Jean knew he liked having things of his own.

Then one exciting day John came running up to the house, shouting for Jean. She ran to him. Had something happened?

Something had. A mother hen had hatched the two eggs which Mr. Andrews had brought home, and now she was taking the baby swans for a walk, one behind the other in a line. As she paraded them proudly, she clucked anxiously. Never had the barnyard seen such chicks.

251

The cygnets, as the young swans are called, soon found the lake. The mother hen clucked and pushed and flapped her wings, but the cygnets would go in the water. She darted excitedly up and down the shore.

The cygnets sailed happily off where she could not follow. Her chicks were doing what not one chick had ever done before. They were swimming!

Jean named the swans Cobby and Penny. They learned to follow the children about like puppies. They rubbed their long necks against John's knees like kittens.

When the fall came, Jean watched the sky anxiously. She knew the time had come to tell John. "When the birds leave for the winter," she told him, "maybe Cobby and Penny will go with them."

John scowled. "Cobby is mine! I won't let him go. I—I'll tie him up."

"Oh, no, John," Jean said. "The Mountie wouldn't let you do that."

"Who is the Mountie?" asked John, looking puzzled.

"The Mountie is a Canadian policeman," Jean said. "It is against the law in Canada to keep wild birds captive," she added.

At last the day came. Once again the birds gathered on the lake for flight. The blue waters were white with the birds. The air was filled with their ringing call, echoing across the lake, then drifting away.

Cobby and Penny sailed out on the lake with the rest of the wild swans.

The signal was given. The shining white birds took off on their flight south.

John scowled up at the sky.

The last birds were gone. The lake was empty. Jean felt tears coming.

Kon—ng—kon—ng! Kon—ng—kon—ng!

Jean and John swung around. The next minute they were down on their knees before Cobby and Penny. Their pets were going to stay!

253

# A Visit from a Mountie

During the second summer Cobby and Penny got their white feathers. Their bills and feet turned black. During this summer, too, John and Jean learned something more about their pets.

One day the family went to town to do some shopping. They were halfway to the village when Mrs. Andrews pointed out something shining in the sunlight, high above them in the sky.

"Penny!" exclaimed Jean.

"Cobby!" shouted John.

"Oh, Daddy, do you think they're flying away?"

Jean and John were so worried about their pets they could hardly stay in the store long enough to buy new clothes. Three times they ran out and looked up into the sky. Each time Penny and Cobby were still there, circling around and around above the roof. When, at last, they all started for home, there were Penny and Cobby, flying ahead, leading the way.

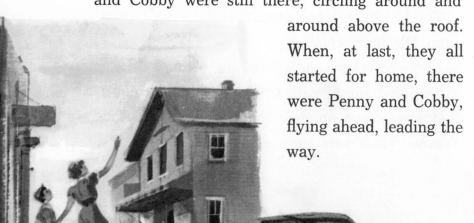

"I don't think they'll ever go away and leave us now," cried John. "I guess they'll stay with us forever." All his fears seemed to have left him.

Then Mr. Andrews got a letter that made him very sad.

"Listen, Jean, and you, John," he said, "this letter is from Sergeant Miller of the Royal Canadian Mounted Police. He says he is coming to see us. Someone has reported to him that we are keeping two wild birds captive. That's against the law."

"Oh, Daddy!" cried Jean. "Will he take Cobby and Penny away from us?"

Mr. Andrews said quietly, "The sergeant is a kind man. He will not take the birds unless he feels he must."

Sergeant Miller of the Royal Canadian Mounted Police arrived on Saturday morning.

"Hello," the Mountie said.

John hung back scowling, but Jean ran and caught his hand. "Please, please, sir, you may have Penny, but do not take Cobby. Cobby is John's. Please, please don't take Cobby away from him."

The Mountie patted her head. "Suppose we see the birds," he said.

Jean looked at John.

"Cobby! Penny!" John called. The birds came to them.

The Mountie smiled when the swans arched their necks and rubbed their heads against Mr. Andrews. He laughed aloud when Cobby pulled a handkerchief out of John's pocket.

Jean showed the Mountie the mother hen, and the place they thought Cobby and Penny might be planning to build a nest three or four summers from now. She told the Mountie how the birds followed them to town.

Later the Mountie sat on the porch, writing busily, while Mrs. Andrews got dinner. Jean and John watched him and worried.

After dinner the Mountie handed Mr. Andrews a paper. "You may be interested in this copy of my report, sir," he said politely. Then he got into the car and drove away.

The family sat on the porch, and Mr. Andrews read the copy of Sergeant Miller's report aloud.

"The trumpeter swans were seen by the writer in the barnyard. They are tame, so tame that they can be petted. Like a cat or a puppy they rub their heads against your knees. They seem to like being with the children of the family, John and Jean. When the family go to town, they fly over the car, circle around the store, and fly back to the farm with them. Cobby and Penny, as the children call the swans, can come and go as they please, but they seem to like to stay in the barnyard. They are in good condition and not in any way captive. There seems to be no reason to take these tame swans away."

"Oh, John," Jean cried. "Cobby and Penny can stay. No one can take them away now!"

*Zillah K. Macdonald*

257

# Ducks' Ditty

All along the backwater,
Through the rushes tall,
Ducks are a-dabbling,
Up tails all!

Ducks' tails, drakes' tails,
Yellow feet a-quiver,
Yellow bills all out of sight
Busy in the river!

Slushy green undergrowth
Where the roach swim—
Here we keep our larder,
Cool and full and dim.

Everyone for what he likes!
We like to be
Heads down, tails up,
Dabbling free!

High in the blue above
Swifts whirl and call—
We are down a-dabbling
Up tails all!

*Kenneth Grahame*

258

# Sur-Dah, the Lion

He made no sound as he moved through the tall breadfruit trees. The soft green underfoot was like a carpet. He was on the hunt—a special kind of hunt.

Sur-Dah was a lion, almost grown. He was big and powerful, but still young. There were many dangers awaiting him on the African veld that he had not yet learned about.

Now it was late afternoon, and he was hungry. He planned to find a wildebeest for his dinner if it took all night.

He left the breadfruit trees and came out into the open veld, near a water hole. Sur-Dah knew that there would be a wildebeest at the water hole. All the animals of the veld came there to drink.

Suddenly Sur-Dah saw something that made him flatten his powerful body to the ground. A lone baboon was sitting only a short distance away on a flat rock. He was very large, and he looked fierce. His brightly colored face was hairless, and long sharp teeth showed in his open mouth.

Beyond the flat rock, Sur-Dah could see many baboons. They were feeding quietly on berries, tender young grass, and bugs. The lone baboon was keeping watch over them.

Sur-Dah slipped behind some brush to think things over. He had seen baboons before, but his mother had always walked a wide circle around them. This should have been a warning to him, but suddenly Sur-Dah forgot all about the wildebeest he had planned to eat for his dinner. Here was something new, something exciting. Nothing about the baboon alerted him to danger. Curiosity got the better of him.

Slowly Sur-Dah circled the rock at a safe distance until the breeze was in his nose. Then with great care he crept, almost flat against the ground, closer to the baboon. Its back was turned to Sur-Dah.

Nearer and nearer Sur-Dah crept toward the baboon. Now he was out in the open. The baboon reached a hairy arm around to scratch his back. He was not really asleep, but the afternoon sun was warm on him, and it had made him a little sleepy. He wasn't watching as sharply as he should have been.

Sur-Dah's yellow eyes flashed. The baboon had long, powerful arms. Yet he was no more than half the lion's size, so he could hardly be expected to put up a real fight.

If he did—well, Sur-Dah would like a good fight! For many days he had stalked game which had fled from him in fear. A good fight to the death might even be a welcome change.

He continued moving carefully until he was only the length of a short jump from the flat rock. He would have to jump up as the rock was higher than his head. The baboon continued to look sleepily to one side and scratch himself. Beyond the rock, rose the low chatter of the other baboons feeding there. None of them looked around.

Sur-Dah measured the distance, his tail moving slowly from side to side. First he took one leap and then sprang. His body rose from the ground as if on wings. He easily cleared the edge of the rock and rushed at the baboon.

Then something happened.

The baboon was not there. Warned by the fall of a stone which Sur-Dah had loosened in his leap, the creature made a sharp sound, whirled about, and sprang straight up into the air.

This rattled Sur-Dah. He stopped. The next thing he knew, the watchman had come down with a thud on his back. The lion felt the sharp, burning pain of the baboon's teeth sinking into his side.

Anger and surprise stirred about equally inside Sur-Dah. He had not expected that this monkey, half his size, would try to fight him. He was used to meeting animals that fled from him, for he was greatly feared.

The pain of the baboon's attack made the lion fiercely angry. With a snarl he turned to kill the baboon and that quickly. But the watchman, with a swiftness equal to Sur-Dah's, leaped aside and sprang straight into the air again. And again he came down with his teeth driving into the lion's side.

"Oof-oof-oof! Oof-oof-oof!" The baboon was barking deep in his throat. Though Sur-Dah did not know it, that bark was a call to the rest of the baboons on the other side of the rock.

The baboons heard the watchman's cries of warning. The mothers took their babies safely out of the way and stayed beside them. The other baboons, bellowing deep in their throats, made for the rock. Their little eyes were red with anger.

Out of the corner of his eye Sur-Dah saw them coming. He turned, ready for the battle.

Just as Sur-Dah was about to leap from the rock and meet the oncoming pack, the watchman came at him again. Though blood was running from a slash Sur-Dah had given him, he fought without a whimper, as bravely as ever.

Suddenly the baboon leaped down from the rock, leaving Sur-Dah all alone upon it. At that minute a rain of fist-sized stones came rushing through the air. Some of them fell against the rock. Others struck Sur-Dah so sharply that he roared in surprise and pain.

The oncoming baboons were picking up sticks and stones—anything they could lay their hairy hands on—and throwing them at him!

Then they were on him in a swarm. Sur-Dah slashed and snarled, wild with anger and pain. Still they continued to swarm around him, making the veld bellow with their angry cries.

Sur-Dah was in the very middle of a cyclone of hairy, powerful arms and legs, of teeth that cut and slashed him. When he attacked the baboons dancing in front of him, two others leaped to his back. They were in a battle to the death if need be.

Sur-Dah rolled over, trying to get rid of them, and came swiftly to his feet to attack again. With a mighty blow and a snarl he sent one of the baboons flying to the ground below the rock, but at his back were a dozen more. He couldn't fight this cyclone in all directions at once.

Sur-Dah was getting winded. He still fought bravely, but the enemy were too many for him. He had struck down and got rid of two more, but others, equally fierce, swarmed about him, bellowing, leaping onto his back, and slashing at his legs. The baboons were clever. They fought in a circle. When Sur-Dah tried to get rid of the enemy in front of him, there were always others behind him to take up the battle.

By now Sur-Dah had been wounded in dozens of places. His wounds were bleeding, for some were deep. He had lost so much blood that he could feel himself growing weaker.

Groaning with pain and anger, he cleared a path through the baboons in front of him and jumped. He fell heavily on his side with a hollow grunt. From somewhere a little strength flowed through his body. He rolled over onto his feet and in a second was up and away.

The baboons ran after him for a short distance. One of them picked up a large rock and slung it with all his might at the running lion.

It struck Sur-Dah hard.

The lion groaned, but did not stop until he was a long distance from that unhappy spot and the terrible cyclone his curiosity had brought upon him. Then he found a soft hollow at the foot of a tree and lay down with a whimper that was almost a groan. His wounds would heal in time, but he had learned something this day—something that he would not forget as long as he lived. Never again would he attack a baboon. Not if the baboon's friends were around!

*Theodore J. Waldeck*

# When You Go to the Zoo

## *Hot, Cold, Dry, Wet*

When you go to the zoo, you see animals that have come from all sorts of places, from all over the world. You see camels from hot, dry desert lands. You see polar bears from the cold north. There are hippos from jungle waters, goats from steep rocky mountains, elephants and chimpanzees from tropical jungles, and giraffes from African grasslands. Some like it hot, some like it cold, some like it dry, and some like it wet.

The place where an animal lives is called his environment. Some zoo animals come from a desert, some come from a jungle, and a wonderful thing about all these animals is that each one is well fitted to live in his special environment. We say that animals are adapted (that means fitted) to live in their own special places.

Rocky Mountain goats couldn't get along at all in the tropical jungle where the hippo is happy. The hippo couldn't last trying to live high on a rocky mountain. Polar bears would die in a desert. Camels couldn't live in the ice and snow of the Far North.

Wherever an animal lives, he must be adapted, or fitted, to live in that environment. He must be built for getting and eating food that grows in that special place. He must be built so that he can travel from one place to another, and he must be built so that he can protect himself against his enemies.

269

# The Hippo Likes Swampy Jungle Lands

If you go to the zoo and stop to look at a hippo, you may say to yourself, "Boy, what a clumsy animal! Wonder how much he weighs—three or four tons?"

The hippo may appear to be clumsy and may weigh several tons, but he is far from being clumsy. He is well fitted for living in water, getting food, and taking care of himself.

When the hippo does not want a drink, his big tongue slips back and closes his throat. You could throw a pail of water into that big mouth, and none of it would go down unless the hippo wanted a drink.

Look at the teeth and tusks. Far back in his throat are big flat teeth. They chew the food so that it can be swallowed. The big tusks at the front are not for chewing at all. They are long and curved and very handy for digging up plants and other food from the bottom of the swamp waters where the hippo lives, and for uprooting plants along the shores of rivers. The pair of tusks at the side of his mouth are very useful to protect the hippo from enemies.

270

Before the hippo goes under water, he takes a deep breath, closes his mouth, his nose, and his eyes, and lays back his ears. Then under he goes. He can swim when he wants to, but usually he just walks around on the bottom.

Once under the water he opens his mouth, for his tongue keeps water from going down his throat. He opens his eyes, too, but he keeps his nose closed tightly. He can look for food under water and be very comfortable because of the way he is built. He can even stay down there for twelve minutes or more, but don't you try that! You are not built for staying under that long.

In zoos many people look into the huge water tank that is the hippo's home and say, "There's nothing in there." Nothing but a three-ton animal lying in the water with only his eyes, ears, and nose out! The hippo's color makes him hard to see if the water is a little muddy. He has a very handy way of blending with his tropical-jungle environment. You can scarcely tell him from the place where he lives.

The hippo is only one of many animals that blend into their environment.

## The Polar Bear Lives in the Arctic

Of course a hippo would find it impossible to live where the polar bear lives. He would be dead from the cold in no time. He couldn't find the kind of food he needs. He is not built for living in the cold waters of the Far North, but the polar bear is. Look at the polar bear in the zoo, and you may be able to discover how he is fitted for a cold environment.

Compare his structure with the structure of other bears. You see that his head is pointed and that his neck and body are longer. This body shape helps him to slip through the water with the greatest of ease. He's a strong swimmer.

If you look closely at his fur coat, you will see that it is very thick. It may be that he takes in his stride even the coldest weather and the iciest water because he is so well protected.

Watch him jump from one rock to another or climb up from the water to the land. It is easy to see that he has strong legs. Listen to him walk. You can't hear anything, can you? That's because the undersides of his paws are covered with hair. It makes him a quiet walker, so it is easier for him to steal up on seals or other animals and surprise them.

Polar bears are hard to see on ice and snow. Their whiteness blends in with the place where they live. In this way the bear is protected against his enemies and is not so easily seen by animals he is trying to catch. His color protects him and helps him to hunt.

The zoo is a wonderful place to see how color helps to protect animals. Look at the animals and compare the places where they live.

Hippos are hard to see in their natural homes, and so are polar bears.

## The Camel Lives in Desert Lands

The hippo and the polar bear would not fit very well into the place where the camel lives. They don't have to. Camels live in the place for which they are built—in the desert.

Deserts are sandy. Some deserts are very hot, and it may surprise you to know that a desert in Asia is very cold. Hot or cold, the desert is a place that suits a camel.

274

You may have noticed that there are camels with one hump and camels with two humps. The two-humped camel has a heavy coat of woolly fur and can live in the cold desert of Asia. The one-humped camel has skin that is almost bare. It would freeze on the very cold Asian desert.

Both kinds of camels are built to get along in sand, even if the wind blows, as it often does. Their feet are large and flat. These flat feet act on the sand somewhat as snowshoes act on the snow. They keep the camel's feet on top of the sand.

The structure of the camel's eye is very interesting, too. The camel has long lashes and heavy lids. The lashes shade his eyes from the bright sun, and the heavy lids protect them from the hard grains of wind-blown sand. A camel needs his long lashes and heavy eyelids when he travels the desert.

275

Water is often a very scarce thing on the desert. The camel is well fitted to get along without it. He has special stomach space for storing up water when it is plentiful. He can use this water as he needs it. In this way he can get along very well without drinking for several days. When at last he reaches a water hole, he can take a long, long drink.

Food is sometimes scarce on the desert, too. Only hard, dry bushes grow there. You might think that such plants are not worth much for food, but camels eat them and like them. Camels couldn't live on the wet plants that a hippo likes.

A camel can go several days without eating a square meal. When there is plenty of food, a camel gets fat. He stores the fat in his hump. When he must go a long time without food, he uses up the fat in his hump.

You can see that a camel is a good example of an animal that is fitted to live in the desert, where it must walk on loose sand, where the food is sometimes not very plentiful, and where it sometimes has to go a long way to get water. That is no place for a hippo or for a polar bear, and you never see either one of them there.

Camels, hippos, and polar bears are good examples of zoo animals that are adapted for living in their natural environments. Their structures help them to eat the food that's there, to get from one place to another, and to protect themselves.

Compare the different animals in the zoo, and you will find that each kind is built to fit into his natural environment. You will see, too, that the animals' homes at the zoo are built to fit them, and that they are given just the right kind of food to suit them. If you want to see more of this:

Watch the anteater eat.

See the seal move through the water.

Watch the penguin swim.

Look at the lion eat meat.

See the elephant drink water.

Watch the monkeys climb and swing.

You can see all these things when you go to the zoo.

*Glenn O. Blough and Marjorie H. Campbell*

277

# Things to Think About and Do

1. In this unit you have read stories and poems about animals from different parts of the world. Look through the unit again to find clues to the place where each animal lived. List each animal, the part of the world he comes from, and the best clues to that place.

2. How much alike are the animals you have read about in this unit? How different are they? To answer these questions, make a chart showing the likenesses and the differences. Under the name of each animal list the following:

|  | LION | HIPPO |
|---|---|---|
| Where it lives |  |  |
| What it eats |  |  |
| How it protects itself | *Do not write in your book* |  |
| How it looks |  |  |

3. Suppose that you work for a magazine and have been sent to Africa to take pictures of animals. Make a list of ten pictures that you will want to take and bring home to use with a story about the veld.

278

4. Rewrite the following sentences, using the words at the left in the place of one or more of the words in each sentence.

remain    She could stay under the water.
weary     She was tired. Her feet ached.
adapted   The camel is a good example of an animal
          fitted to live in the desert.
cygnet    The young swan soon found the lake.
tropical  There were hippos from hot swampy jungles.
alert     He has many enemies in the forest and must
          always be watchful.
whimper   He gave a low cry, almost a groan.
expect    He did not look for that to happen.

5. Suppose someone sent you a penguin, an anteater, or one of the other animals listed below for your birthday. Make a list of problems you might have in keeping each of them at home.

| baby hippo | otter | penguin |
| baby lion | snake | anteater |

6. Read more about one of the animals you have met in this unit. Use the encyclopedia and books about animals. Then plan a talk about this animal. Give your talk as part of a class program.

7. Look for other poems about animals. Choose one to share with your friends.

# Some Books to Read

*Blue Canyon Horse*, by Ann Nolan Clark.

This unusual tale is about a Utah Indian boy's love for his beautiful horse.

*Burma Boy*, by Willis Lindquist.

When Majda Koom, the mighty elephant, runs away, Haji braves many dangers to find him.

*Eight Rings on His Tail*, by John Oldrin.

There is humor in the exciting adventures of Patches, the raccoon with eight handsome rings on his tail.

*Elf Owl*, by Mary and Conrad Buff.

From his perch in the top of a saguaro cactus the smallest owl watches desert life.

*See Through the Forest*, by Millicent Selsam.

In this book the forest is like an apartment house with the woodland folk living at different levels from basement to penthouse.

*Whooping Crane*, by Robert McClung.

This is the beautiful story of a bird that has almost disappeared from the earth.

*Zoo Pets* and *Zoo Celebrities*, by William Bridges.

These stories about animals at the zoo are true to life.

# Fun and Nonsense

# Freddy, the Detective

"Call yourself a detective!" said Jinx, the cat. "Why, pig, you couldn't find your own nose in the dark!"

Freddy, the pig, had just announced to the animals of the Bean farm that he was going to become a detective.

"Think of all the good I could do," he said. "Right this very minute Simon, the rat, is stealing grain from the barn. We all know it, but who can prove it? A little detective work would bring Simon's thieving ways out into the open. Then Mr. Bean could take steps."

"I thought he took steps all the time," said Mrs. Wiggins, the cow. Mrs. Wiggins had a heart of gold, but she wasn't very bright.

"That's a way of saying that he would go into action," Freddy said. "He would go into action against Simon. Take steps to do something about him. Understand, Mrs. Wiggins?"

Before she could answer, Charlie, the rooster, flapped his wings and stretched his neck forward as far as it would go. "Very well put, Freddy," he crowed. "Very well put. As for the detective business, it seems to me—"

"Oh, dry up, Charlie," said Jinx. "All you ever do is crow."

Charlie looked hurt and didn't crow again for almost five minutes.

"What gave you the idea that you could be a detective, pig?" asked Jinx.

"I feel it," said Freddy. "I've read lots and lots of detective stories, and I can almost always figure out how they are going to end. Sometimes I know the end before the detective in the story does."

Jinx grinned around his whiskers. "That wouldn't be because you looked at the end first, would it?" he asked.

"No, it wouldn't," said Freddy warmly. "I just happen to have what it takes to make a good detective."

Jinx looked long at Freddy's round figure and said nothing for several seconds. Then he rose and stretched.

"Tell you what, pig," he said, "I'll make you a little bet."

All the animals came closer so as not to miss a word. They liked Freddy well enough, but they had respect for Jinx's good sense. It wouldn't be likely that Jinx would decide to make a bet he couldn't win.

284

Freddy looked sharply at Jinx. "What's the big idea?"

"Do you know where Macy's pond is?" asked Jinx.

"I've known that all my life," said Freddy.

"Well," said Jinx, "if you can find the pond, blindfolded, I'll give you this red velvet cushion that I sleep on."

"Now look, Jinx," Freddy began, "I haven't time—"

"My fine, soft, thick, red velvet cushion," said Jinx. "Just think how that would dress up the pigpen. If you don't find the pond—"

Freddy made up his mind. "I'll find it all right. You don't have to think up something for me to do if I lose. I'll find the pond, and blindfolded."

"Oh, yes," said the cat. "I thought you'd try that. No, if you don't find the pond, then you'll have to—let's see—you'll have to take me to the movies in town and buy me a chocolate soda."

Freddy weighed the velvet cushion against the movies and soda for a minute. Then he said, "All right, it's a bet."

Freddy stood in the middle of the barnyard. All the other animals stood around and watched while Jinx tied a handkerchief over his eyes. Then they all closed in on him and turned him around four or five times so he would lose his sense of direction. They moved about, too, so their voices wouldn't come from the places where he had seen them standing.

Then Jinx said, "Go!"

Freddy was not a detective for nothing. To reach that pond he had to go out of the gate, cross the road and get through the fence on the other side, then cut across a valley to another road. When he had crossed this road, he would be in the meadow on the Macy farm.

286

If he kept on in the same direction, he was sure he would pass near the pond. Like most animals he could smell water, and he knew he wouldn't have much trouble finding it.

As for starting out in the right direction, and holding to it all the way, there was nothing much to that. For what breeze there was came in light puffs always from the west. He had only to keep it on his right cheek and he couldn't go wrong.

He waited a minute until the breeze came stronger. It was on his left cheek. He turned around and started out, and there was a low chattering from the animals, but Jinx put a stop to that.

"Hey, be quiet, will you?" he said. "Of course he can find the pond if you're going to keep telling him when he's going right. You can follow along, but keep still, or we'll call the whole thing off." After that, they kept still.

So Freddy went out of the gate. He crossed the road, and the ditch beyond it, and got through the fence. Then he started down the gentle slope, stopping now and then until another puff of wind came against his right cheek and proved to him that he was still going south.

All the floor of this valley was one big hayfield, so there were no trees or fences for him to run into. He would have reached the Macy farm all right. Maybe he would have found the pond too—only just before he got to the bottom of the slope, the wind began to shift.

It shifted slowly around toward the south, each puff a little weaker and a little farther around. Freddy, as he went along, steering by the feel of it on his right cheek, shifted with the wind.

Pretty soon he was headed east, up the valley, instead of south, across it. He was at the bottom now, on level ground, so he didn't notice anything. The breeze died away, the air was perfectly still.

Freddy stood perfectly still, too, waiting. He could hear the other animals breathing and moving around a little behind him, but that didn't tell him anything. Then a puff of wind came. It was from dead ahead—from the east, though of course he didn't know that.

He turned until it was on his right cheek and went on. In a minute, sure enough, the ground began to slope up. Now he was walking along right back the way he had come.

Some of the animals who were following him began to laugh, but Jinx flattened his ears and stared so fiercely that they quieted down. Freddy went on, felt his way through the fence and across the road, and across the Bean fence a little way up from the gate.

Up the hill past the barnyard he went, missing his own home, the pigpen, by only a few yards. Then he put his nose up in the air and sniffed. "I smell water, and it's not soda water," he said. "Better bring out that velvet cushion, cat—it'll be mine in another few minutes."

Freddy could smell water all right, but it wasn't the Macy pond—it was the big duck pond on his own farm. Mr. Bean's two white ducks were swimming around on it. Their Uncle Wesley, a pompous little duck who had come to live with them, was nodding in the shade on the bank. He didn't hear Freddy coming.

When the blindfolded pig walked slowly up to the edge of the water and stopped, he stepped squarely on the pompous little duck's left foot.

Uncle Wesley woke with an outraged quack, forgetting his dignity

Freddy pulled off the handkerchief. "Oh, I'm sorry," he said. "Very careless of me." He looked around. "I didn't know that Mr. Macy kept ducks down here. A fine place! Looks very much like our own duck pond, over on the Bean farm."

Then he stared hard at Uncle Wesley. "Why you—you're Uncle Wesley! What on earth are you doing down here?"

"Sir," said the duck, who was trying to recover his dignity while hopping around on one foot—not an easy thing to do, "sir, I am minding my own business, and I suggest that you do the same."

"Well," said Freddy, "that's what I—"

"My dear sir," Uncle Wesley said pompously, "your business, whatever it is, does not allow you to come up here with a silly handkerchief over your eyes. It does not allow you to tramp all over the dignity of a person who is sitting quietly in his own front yard. It's an outrage, a perfect outrage."

"But—" Freddy began.

291

The duck stopped him again and went on, still hopping about, "I have my rights, and I shall stand on them."

"Well, all right," said Freddy, "go on, do it, and stop jumping around. I can't talk to anybody who won't stand still. What did you have for lunch—grasshoppers?" He turned to Jinx. "How did these ducks get over here, anyway? How—" He stopped, for the animals began to laugh as if at a huge joke.

It took some time to prove to Freddy what had happened. Even after he figured out how, steered by the shifting wind, he had walked right around in a half circle and come back to the place he had started from, he felt all turned around.

"I can't understand it," he said, looking out across the valley toward the Macy farm. "I can't be two places at once, and yet I know this is Macy's pond, and yet—yet I can see I'm here—"

"O.K., pig," said Jinx. "You can take it from us you're here. And I can tell you where you'll be a few nights from now—you'll be in front of the ticket window at the movies, asking for two good seats."

*Walter R. Brooks*

# The Cowardly Baseball

## *As Told by Uncle Fritz*

Bob and Cary thought their Uncle Fritz the very best storyteller in the world. Whenever he came to visit them, they hung around hoping for a story. Best of all, Uncle Fritz's stories were funny.

Usually, right after he had lunch, he'd feel a story coming on. He would sit down in the big chair by the window and say, "As I remember, it happened this way."

At those words Bob dropped the catcher's mitt he had just slipped on, and Cary forgot all about whatever she was planning to do. Each of them would sit down on the floor, facing Uncle Fritz, and he would wink once at Bob and once at Cary and begin.

It happened just this way the day he told them the story of *The Cowardly Baseball*.

It was all rather strange (began Uncle Fritz), for I wasn't really watching the baseball game in New York that day. I was walking around outside the fence when the baseball sailed over. It sailed so high over the grandstand that it went on over the street, hit the top of a brick building, and bounced all the way back.

As I picked it up, one of the ticket-sellers standing by the gate saw me. "You're lucky, Mister," he said. "The great Babe Ruth just hit a home run. He really hit that one."

I felt very proud to own a baseball that Babe
Ruth had hit. You children are too young to
remember, but the Babe was one of the greatest
players who ever lived. They say he could hit a
home run all the way from New York to Boston.

I kept the ball and showed it to all my friends.
One fellow was more interested than the others.
He was a young man named Carl Skedaddle, and
he was quite a baseball player himself. He was
the star of a team called the Wasps.

The Wasps were a bunch of young fellows who
played for our town against teams from other
nearby towns. Their club was famous for never
winning a game. They hadn't even come close to
winning a game. Once, though, they held Turkeytown to a score of 24–1, so the Wasps had hopes.

"We're having a practice this afternoon," Carl
told me as he turned my Babe Ruth baseball over
in his hand. "Let me borrow this ball for the
practice. I'd like to hit it just once, so I can say
that Babe Ruth and I both hit the same ball."

"I'll come along," I said, "and bring the ball with me. Can't take any chances of losing it."

The whole team of Wasps was at the ball park when I got there. Billy Blepper was their pitcher and the manager of the team. He was five feet tall and weighed over three hundred pounds.

When Carl saw me, he asked to let me take Billy's place on the pitching mound. "He's got a baseball with which Babe Ruth hit a home run," Carl told Billy. "I want to hit it once, to give me luck."

Billy grunted. "You'll have to have luck to hit it. Skedaddle, you haven't hit anything for two weeks."

Carl seemed to be hurt and said with dignity, "I got on base once in last week's game, didn't I?"

"Sure," said Billy, "you got hit by a pitched ball."

"I could have jumped out of the way, couldn't I? Let him pitch the Babe Ruth ball."

Billy Blepper looked at me and said, "O.K. Maybe you might be able to hit it if this old fellow pitches."

I was a little angry at the manager's words. So he thought I was an old man, did he? Well, I'd show him that I was no butter fingers.

296

I pulled back my arm, ready to throw, and got
a crick in my back. It hurt a lot, but I let on I
always bent over to throw.

I don't know how pitchers can throw clear to
home plate from the pitcher's mound. I couldn't.
The ball went about halfway.

"Come on in close," Carl Skedaddle called. He
was swinging a large bat, ready for action.

I went closer and closer until I could almost
touch Carl. Then I threw the ball. As Carl swung
his bat, the funniest thing happened! That Babe
Ruth ball ducked. Yes, sir, it dropped under the
bat, curved up, stopped, and came back to me.

Carl Skedaddle swallowed hard. "Get back a
ways," he said, recovering from his surprise.

I did and threw the ball again. This time it circled around Carl's neck, and dropped to the ground. The day was cool, but big drops stood out on Carl's nose and forehead. He had missed by a good three feet.

"That's a mean curve you throw, Mister," grunted Billy Blepper.

The way that cowardly baseball twisted and turned was something to see. It didn't want to get hit. After the way Babe Ruth had smacked it, that ball wasn't taking any chances.

I pitched to every man on the Wasps' team, but nobody hit the ball. Before I knew what was going on, Billy Blepper had me signed up to pitch for the Wasps against Turkeytown on Saturday.

The manager wanted me to practice with the others, but I begged off. I didn't want any more cricks in my back needlessly. I had one and was limping on a sore foot.

# The Big Game

Two or three people cheered when I walked out on the pitching mound to start the game. They were from Turkeytown, so I didn't let their cheering go to my head. It is never wise to think too well of yourself.

My feet hurt, so I took my shoes off before pitching the first ball. I didn't think I'd be running around any.

The umpire called, "Play ball!" or something like that. I pulled the Babe Ruth ball out of my pocket—the ball that was afraid of being hit—and threw it to the batter. He swung at it, and got his arms all twisted up trying to follow the twists of the ball and smack it. The ball kept well out of range.

The umpire had to untie him, and the game went on. For six and a half innings not one Turkeytown player touched the ball. Needless to say, I didn't let their pitcher use the same baseball I was using. Nobody but me knew that the ball was afraid. They seemed to think I was a very good pitcher.

I got rather tired standing up along about the fifth inning, so I sat down on the ground and threw the ball from there. It worked just as well.

We were giving Turkeytown a real beating, you see, but for one thing. Our team couldn't get on base either. The Turkeytown pitcher didn't need a Babe Ruth baseball because the Wasps couldn't seem to hit any kind of baseball.

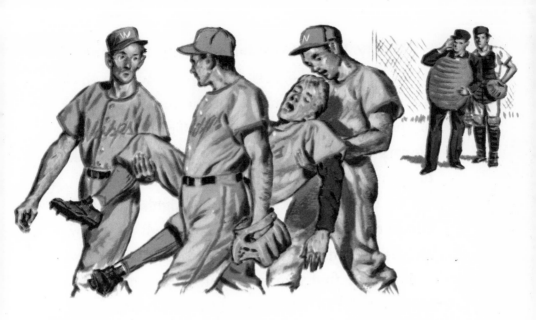

In the last of the seventh inning, Carl Skedaddle took a great swing and got hit on the head by the ball. This put him on first base, and he was the first player on either side to get that far. Three of the Wasps carried him to first base and set him down there.

"Don't you want somebody to run for him?" the umpire asked Billy Blepper.

"What for?" Billy answered. "He won't have to move."

Billy was right. The next three Wasps struck out, and we took the field. Carl remained flat on his back, but it was all right. He was the first baseman, and that's where he was.

Nobody had scored yet when the other team came to bat in the first half of the twenty-third inning. It was the middle of the night, and most of the crowd had gone home. The Turkeytown players wanted to stop, but our boys didn't like to miss a chance of winning a game for once.

The baseball park didn't have lights, but Billy Blepper had burning candles stuck all over him, and he lighted up the place like a Christmas tree.

I got the first two men out. Then something happened. The ball went up to the plate as usual, the batter swung, and the next thing I knew, the ball was sailing far over the fence for a home run.

What was funny about it was that the Turkeytown batter hadn't hit the ball at all. It just flew away, rather than be smacked again.

We never found the Babe Ruth ball. When Billy Blepper took my place as pitcher, Turkeytown had scored thirty runs. The game ended 47–0.

I had a crick in my back and was sore all over, but not as sore as Carl Skedaddle. After all, (Uncle Fritz winked at Bob and Cary) Carl had been run over forty-seven times while he was stretched out on first base.

*Charles Williams*

# Mister Penny

## In the Neighbor's Garden

Once there was an old man. His name was Mister Penny. He lived in a wreck of a shed by a path that led to the village of Wuddle.

Even though Mister Penny worked year after year in the factory of Wuddle, he spent all his money buying food for his family of animals. He had a horse and a cow and a goat and a pig and a lamb and a hen and a rooster.

They were all lazy, and Mister Penny had to work very hard to feed them. They would do nothing for themselves.

One morning in early summer, after Mister Penny had gone to the factory, Doody, the rooster, started crowing. Then he flew to the shed roof.

303

"Cock-a-doodle-do," he crowed. "I can see farther than any of you!"

"Well, if you can see so much," said Splop, the goat, "tell us what's growing in the neighbor's garden."

Doody named everything he saw that was good to eat and some things he didn't see.

"Mmmmmmm," said Mooloo, the cow. "That's the kind of food I like."

"Too bad it belongs to somebody else," said Limpy, the horse.

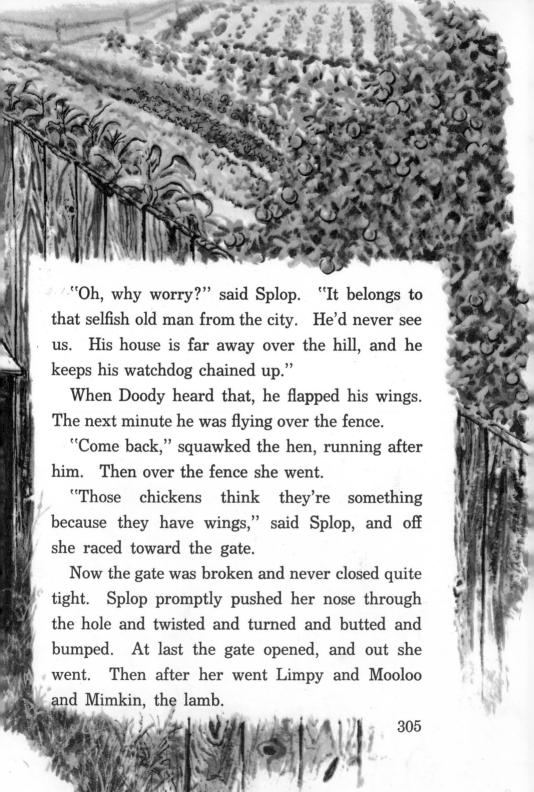

"Oh, why worry?" said Splop. "It belongs to that selfish old man from the city. He'd never see us. His house is far away over the hill, and he keeps his watchdog chained up."

When Doody heard that, he flapped his wings. The next minute he was flying over the fence.

"Come back," squawked the hen, running after him. Then over the fence she went.

"Those chickens think they're something because they have wings," said Splop, and off she raced toward the gate.

Now the gate was broken and never closed quite tight. Splop promptly pushed her nose through the hole and twisted and turned and butted and bumped. At last the gate opened, and out she went. Then after her went Limpy and Mooloo and Mimkin, the lamb.

But not Pugwug, the pig! He had been in such a hurry that he had tried to push through a hole under the fence.

"Wait for me," he squealed. "Wait for me!"

Nobody heard Pugwug. They were already in the neighbor's garden, eating everything up, even the leaves and the blossoms.

"Mmm," said Mooloo when she had eaten so many young cornstalks she didn't seem to care for any more. She went over to Limpy, who was near the apple trees. "What's the matter?" she asked, for Limpy had stopped chewing apples and stood with his ears straight up, listening hard.

"What's the matter?" Mooloo asked again.

Limpy didn't answer. He lifted his head still higher and looked back over the hill. There it was—the dog he had heard! Behind the dog came the neighbor himself with a whip.

"Run!" Limpy shouted. "Run!"

Chukluk, the hen, started running in circles. "Oh, he'll catch us! Catch us! Catch us!" she squawked, but soon she found the fence and flew home safely.

The others all ran through the gate—all but Doody. And the gate swung shut behind them. Doody stayed where he was until the dog could see him.

"Just wait until I catch you," growled the dog, and on he came after the rooster.

Doody laughed and crowed as he ran along the bushes by the fence. Even when it was time to fly over, he stopped and crowed back, "Catch me, bossy old Big Teeth!"

That made the dog so angry that he jumped straight into the air, and he did catch Doody. He caught him by the tail.

For a second the rooster thought he had come to his end. Then he started flapping his wings and tugging. He pulled until his tail came loose. The next thing he knew, he was over the fence, but he had no tail left at all!

The others had no time to watch Doody. The neighbor was there at the gate with his whip. He was pushing and pounding. All at once an old board broke, and in came his head through the hole.

"If he comes any closer, I'll butt him!" said Splop.

When the neighbor saw Splop coming toward him with her head down, ready to butt, he decided he did not want to get in after all. And off he went up the hill.

## Trouble for Everybody

Mimkin began to cry.

"Don't cry now," said Limpy. "He's gone."

"But my stomach!" said Mimkin. "It aches!"

"Mine too-oo!" cried Mooloo.

By now Limpy was beginning to feel such pains from green apples that he couldn't talk. He went off to his bed in the straw, and the others all followed. On their way to the shed Splop saw the tail end of Pugwug under the fence. That poor pig was still stuck fast!

Splop laughed even though her stomach ached. Then she ran to help Pugwug, pawing away dirt until he had room to wiggle out. Pugwug was so tired from squealing he just followed the others to the shed and was soon fast asleep on the floor.

"What's this, what's this?" said Mister Penny when he opened his gate that evening. "None of my family to meet me?"

When he came into the shed and saw them looking so sad, he did not know what to think.

He ran to look at Limpy's tongue.   Then he ran
to Mooloo.   Her tongue hung down like a piece of
wet cotton cloth.

"They're all sick!" said Mister Penny.   He got
a big bottle and a tablespoon and started giving
them sticky medicine.

Pugwug got some, too, though he kicked and
squealed.   He had no aches or pains, and he didn't
want medicine.   His stomach wanted food.

Last of all Mister Penny came to Doody.   He
picked him up from the straw to pour his medicine
in.   "What's this?" he exclaimed.

What could have happened?   All sick at once,
and no tail on the rooster!

He was reading the newspaper that evening when there came a loud knock on the door. "My goggled eyes!" he exclaimed, jumping up to open it. "Who can it be?"

In came the big neighbor, waving his whip and shouting at the top of his voice.

The man's words were popping out like popcorn over a hot fire, and Mister Penny could understand only a few of them. "No tops . . . carrots! New plants . . . buds! Every apple . . . bite in it!"

"It's his garden," thought Mister Penny. "Something's happened to his garden."

Suddenly shivers ran up his back, for he caught the words "hungry pests . . . perfect nuisance . . . good-for-nothing creatures!"

"So that's what made them all sick!" Mister Penny shook his head. "Oh me, oh me!"

"You'd just better do away with those pests," growled the neighbor. "I'll take them myself in pay for their damage—though they're not much good. I suppose the pig might give good meat, and the lamb might make good stew."

"Oh, please!" said Mister Penny. "Not that!'

"Well," growled the neighbor, "I'm behind with my work. If you must keep those pests, here's what you can do. Plow the three south fields before the new moon. Clean out the stones from that pasture land near my pine woods. Cut the grass on my lawn. Then you can bring me milk for the rest of the summer."

He slapped an envelope on the table. "Here's all the damage in writing. Decide overnight which you'll do—give me your hungry beasts, or do this work."

When the neighbor had gone, Mister Penny sat down by his table. "Oh, me!" he said to himself. "Is there nothing I can do to save my family?"

## Limpy Has an Idea

Now Limpy, who had been watching and listening, went over to Mooloo and woke her up. When she heard the story, she almost cried.

"What can we do?" asked Mooloo.

"Well," said Limpy, "I'm not so lame as I've made believe. I can do that plowing as well as any other horse, and there's a collar on that old plow in the corner. I'm going to do the plowing!"

312

"You know," said Mooloo, "I've been giving only about a cupful of milk. I was too lazy to chew my cud, that's why. But I'll chew my cud thirty hours a day before I'll let that mean man take any of us!"

"What's the matter?" crowed Doody.

"Hush!" said Limpy. "People will think it's time to get up before they've gone to bed."

Soon Splop came tumbling over to see what had happened. She was so noisy about it that she woke up Mimkin and Chukluk, but not Pugwug! That pig could sleep through anything.

"Say!" said Splop. "If that old pepperbox ever tries to take me away from Mister Penny, I'll butt him so high that he'll never come down."

313

"Don't talk nonsense," said Limpy. "We damaged his garden, and we have to pay. What work do you choose?"

"I don't choose any!" said Splop. "Of course, if it has to be done, I'll clean out those old stones."

"I'll cut the lawn," said Mimkin.

"I'll lay bigger eggs," said Chukluk.

Splop shook her horns in front of Doody. "What good is a rooster without any tail?" she asked. "All he can do is eat bugs."

That gave Limpy an idea. Doody could follow the plow and save all the worms. Mister Penny never had enough worms at his stand outside the fence for the men who came from the city to fish.

"Well, come on!" said Splop. "Let's go!"

Limpy looked through the hole. Mister Penny had fallen asleep with his head on the table.

Limpy looked out of the window. Everything was black, so he let Splop run ahead to open the gate. Forgetting he'd ever felt lame, Limpy hurried to get the plow. He pushed his head through the collar and handled the plow easily.

"Oh, I almost forgot!" he said. He went over to Pugwug and woke him up. "I need something heavy to hold the plow down. Come!"

314

Out they went into the dark—all but Mooloo and Chukluk, who stayed behind, one to chew her cud and the other to eat some feed.

All through the night Mister Penny sat by his table and painfully tried to think. Whenever he fell asleep, his dreams woke him up.

When morning came, he still didn't know how to save his animals. He went back to look at them. Then he put his stool down beside Mooloo and started to milk.

"Mooloo!" cried Mister Penny after a few minutes. Instead of a cupful of milk, there was a bucketful! He jumped up and threw his arms around Mooloo's neck. "Good Mooloo! If you only knew how much I need this milk!"

The chickens were squawking and crowing, trying to make him look. He went to see if by chance Chukluk had an egg for him. Bending down, he looked closely at something in the straw.

An egg as large as a goose could lay! And a canful of beautiful worms!

Mister Penny cooked the egg for his breakfast. Then he ran out and put the worms on his stand, where he sold them like newspapers. They were two for a penny, and he left a box for the money.

315

Next he put part of the milk into his newest bucket and went up the hill to his neighbor's house. When he knocked gently at the back door, the neighbor came out and said, "Well, old man, I see you have a lot done! If you work as fast every night as you did last night, you'll have it all done before the new moon."

Mister Penny looked around to see what the man was talking about.

The grass on the lawn was cut short. A big pile of stones had been cleaned out from the pasture land. In the fields was a long stretch of newly plowed earth. It was like a soft brown carpet.

"I can't understand it at all!" Mister Penny kept saying to himself as he hurried to the factory.

The next morning everything happened just as it had the day before. More milk! Another giant egg! A canful of beautiful worms! And much more work done at the neighbor's!

"Well, old man," said the neighbor as he took the milk, "you worked so fast you'll have the damage paid for before the new moon."

"I'm jigsawed to a puzzle!" said Mister Penny as he went off to his job in the factory of Wuddle. "Jigsawed to a puzzle! It must be goblins—though I never believed in them before."

On the first night of the new moon Mister Penny's animals came tumbling home all out of breath. They woke up Mooloo. They woke up the hen. "Hurrah! Hurrah! It's all done. The damage is paid for. It's finished!"

"And what now?" said Splop, kicking up her heels as frisky as a colt. "I like to work!"

"Me too," said Mimkin and Doody.

Limpy pulled the plow to its place in the corner and slipped his head out of the collar. "You know," he said, "I've been thinking how stupid we've been —never doing any work! All this time we might have had a garden right here—for ourselves and Mister Penny."

On Monday morning when Mister Penny came out of his shed, his pipe dropped from his mouth. There at one end of his own field the ground had been plowed and piles of stones cleaned out!

"Well, I'm jigsawed to a puzzle! Those good goblins!" he said. "They did all that work for my neighbor. Now they're starting a garden for me."

On Saturday noon Mister Penny hurried home from the factory. He took all the pennies he'd saved from selling the worms and milk—a whole bagful—and he and his family went to market.

First they bought seeds for cabbages, squash, and other vegetables they liked to eat—except horse-radish because you can't make a good meal out of horse-radish. Then they hurried home, and Mister Penny planted everything. Only no horse-radish.

The rains came and the sun was warm. Before very long Mister Penny's garden was the most beautiful garden in the town of Wuddle.

One foggy night when there came a storm, he took his umbrella and went out to see if his garden was all right.

"Well, what on earth?" he exclaimed, for as sure as breathing, there was Limpy, no longer lame, pulling the plow with Pugwug holding it down.

318

Behind walked Doody looking for worms. A little farther over was Splop cleaning out stones. Mimkin was cutting grass!

Mister Penny ran around in the rain, exclaiming, "So you are the goblins and fairies that have been as busy as beavers! With such a garden we'll have more than enough to eat, and I'll no longer need to work in that noisy factory of Wuddle! I can stay right at home and just work in my garden!"

Mister Penny kept on selling worms and milk, and he sold truckloads of stones for filling up holes in the road. Soon he had enough money to build a pink house with a windmill for the wind to play with, and a board for crickets to hide under.

In the long summer evenings the people of Wuddle would look over the low fence and say to each other, "Isn't he a strange one, living in a house with all those animals! But I say, they're the happiest family in Wuddle."

*Marie Hall Ets*

319

# The Five Chinese Brothers

Once upon a time there were Five Chinese Brothers, and they all looked just alike. They lived with their mother in a little house not far from the sea.

The First Chinese Brother could swallow the sea. The Second Chinese Brother had an iron neck. The Third Chinese Brother could stretch and stretch and stretch his legs. The Fourth Chinese Brother could not be burned. The Fifth Chinese Brother could hold his breath for as long as he wished.

Every morning the First Chinese Brother would bid his mother good-by and go fishing. Whatever the weather, he would come back to the village with beautiful fish which he had caught and could sell at the market for a very good price.

One day, as he was leaving the market place, a little boy stopped him and asked if he might go fishing with him.

320

"No, it cannot be done," said the First Chinese Brother.

The little boy begged and begged, and at last the First Chinese Brother said, "You may go if you will promise one thing. Promise to obey me promptly."

"Yes, yes," the little boy promised.

Early next morning the First Chinese Brother and the little boy went down to the shore.

"Remember," said the First Chinese Brother, "you must obey me promptly. When I make a sign for you to come back, you must come at once."

"Yes, yes," the little boy promised.

Then the First Chinese Brother swallowed the sea. All the fish were left high and dry at the bottom of the sea. All the treasures of the sea lay uncovered.

The little boy was delighted. He ran here and there, filling his pockets with wonderful shells and plants which he had never seen before.

Near the shore the First Chinese Brother gathered some clams while he kept holding the sea in his mouth. Soon he grew tired. It is very hard to hold the sea. He made a sign with his hand for the little boy to come back. The little boy saw him, but he paid no attention.

The First Chinese Brother waved his arms to call the boy back.

Did the little boy care? Not a bit, and he ran farther away.

322

The First Chinese Brother felt the sea pushing up inside him. He waved as hard as he could to call the little boy back. The little boy made faces at him and ran as fast as he could the other way, going farther and farther away from the shore.

The First Chinese Brother held the sea until he could stand it no longer. All of a sudden the sea pushed its way out of his mouth and went back to its bed—and the little boy vanished.

When the First Chinese Brother returned to the village alone, he was taken by the police. He was tried and told he was going to have his head cut off.

On the morning he was to die, he said to the judge, "Your Honor, will you allow me to go and bid my mother good-by?"

"It is only fair," said the judge.

So the First Chinese Brother went home—and the Second Chinese Brother came back in his place.

All the people were gathered on the village square to see him killed. The man who was to kill him took a sword and hit him a mighty blow on the neck.

The Second Chinese Brother got up and smiled.

He was the one with the iron neck, and the sharpest sword just could not cut his head off.

Everyone was angry, and they decided that he should be drowned.

On the morning he was to die, the Second Chinese Brother said to the judge, "Your Honor, will you allow me to go and bid my mother good-by?"

"It is only fair," said the judge.

So the Second Chinese Brother went home, and the Third Chinese Brother came back in his place.

He was pushed on a boat, which made for the open sea. When they were far out on the ocean, the Third Chinese Brother was thrown overboard. He began to stretch and stretch his legs far, far down to the bottom of the sea, and all the time his smiling face was bobbing up and down on the waves. He just could not be drowned.

324

Everybody was very angry, and they all decided that he should be burned.

On the morning he was to die, the Third Chinese Brother said to the judge, "Your Honor, will you allow me to go and bid my mother good-by?"

"It is only fair," said the judge.

So the Third Chinese Brother went home, and the Fourth Chinese Brother came back in his place.

He was tied to a big pole. Fire was set to it, and all the people stood around watching. From the middle of the flames they heard him say, "This is quite pleasant."

"Bring some more wood!" the people cried.

The fire roared higher.

"Now it is quite comfortable," said the Fourth Chinese Brother, for he was the one who could not be burned.

Everybody was getting more and more angry, and they all decided he should be smothered.

325

On the morning he was to die, the Fourth Chinese Brother said to the judge, "Your Honor, will you allow me to go bid my mother good-by?"

"It is only fair," said the judge.

So the Fourth Chinese Brother went home, and the Fifth Chinese Brother came back in his place.

A large brick oven had been built on the village square. It looked like a huge beehive, and it had been all filled with whipped cream. The Fifth Chinese Brother was shoveled into the oven, right in the middle of the whipped cream. The door was shut tight, and everybody sat around and waited for him to smother.

They were not going to be tricked again! So they stayed there all night and even a little after dawn, just to make sure.

Then they opened the door and pulled him out. He shook the whipped cream off himself and said, "My! That was a good sleep!"

Everybody stared with open mouth and round eyes. But the judge stepped up and said, "We have found it impossible to kill you. We have tried to cut your head off with a sword, to drown you, to burn you, and to smother you in an oven. Somehow it can't be done. It must be that you did nothing wrong, and should not be killed."

"Yes, yes," shouted all the people. So they let him go, and he went home.

After that the Five Chinese Brothers and their mother all lived together happily for many years.

*Claire Huchet Bishop*
*Kurt Wiese*

327

# The Polar Bear

The Polar Bear is unaware
   Of cold that cuts me through:
For why?   He has a coat of hair.
   I wish I had one too!

*Hilaire Belloc*

# How Doth the Little Crocodile

How doth the little crocodile
   Improve his shining tail,
And pour the waters of the Nile
   On every golden scale!

How cheerfully he seems to grin,
   How neatly spreads his claws,
And welcomes little fishes in
   With gently smiling jaws!

*Lewis Carroll*

328

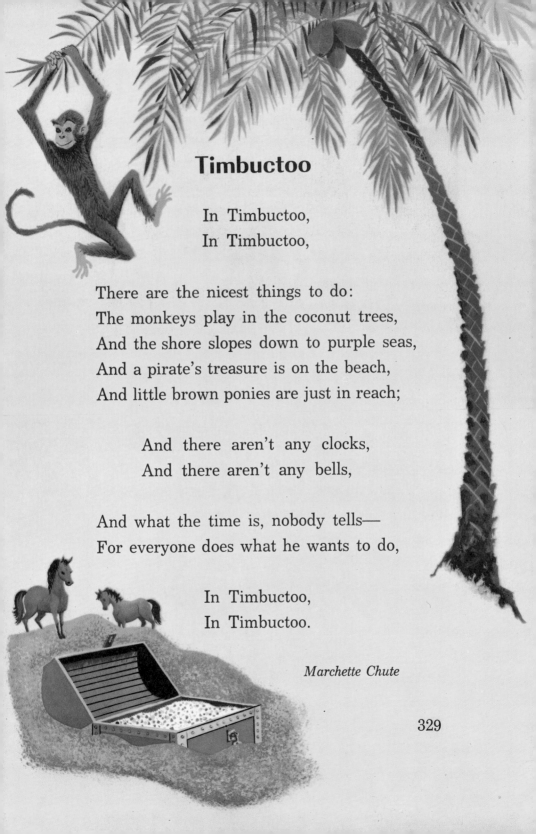

# Timbuctoo

In Timbuctoo,
In Timbuctoo,

There are the nicest things to do:
The monkeys play in the coconut trees,
And the shore slopes down to purple seas,
And a pirate's treasure is on the beach,
And little brown ponies are just in reach;

And there aren't any clocks,
And there aren't any bells,

And what the time is, nobody tells—
For everyone does what he wants to do,

In Timbuctoo,
In Timbuctoo.

*Marchette Chute*

# Jonathan Bing

Poor old Jonathan Bing
Went out in his carriage to visit the King,
But everyone pointed and said, "Look at that!
Jonathan Bing has forgotten his hat!"
(He'd forgotten his hat!)

Poor old Jonathan Bing
Went home and put on a new hat for the King,
But up by the palace a soldier said, "Hi!
You can't see the King; you've forgotten your tie!"
(He'd forgotten his tie!)

330

Poor old Jonathan Bing,
He put on a *beautiful* tie for the King,
But when he arrived an Archbishop said, "Ho!
You can't come to court in pyjamas, you know!"

Poor old Jonathan Bing
Went home and addressed a short note to the King:

If you please will excuse me
I won't come to tea;
For home's the best place for
All people like me!

*Beatrice Curtis Brown*

# Things to Think About and Do

1. Make a picture map of the Bean farm and Macy's pond as you think they looked. Then show in red the path Freddy took across the valley. Put a blue star on the spot where the wind began to shift and Freddy turned back toward home.

2. Think of a funny sentence that will tell something about your map. Then write the sentence under it.

3. Make a dictionary of words that are used to describe a baseball game. Then as a reporter for a newspaper, write a short story about a ball game. Use words from your baseball dictionary.

4. You may wish to work with two or three others in your class and make a mural of the stories in this unit. Before you start work on your mural, decide which part of the story you will show. When the mural is finished, display it in the library corner.

5. Write a different ending for either the story about Mister Penny or the story about the cowardly baseball. Suppose the Babe Ruth ball had landed on the moon. How would that story have ended?

332

6. Hold an election to decide which characters in the stories from this unit are

the kindest  
the laziest  
the most helpful  
the most tricky  
the most pompous  
the most scornful  

Before the election, plan talks about the candidates you choose. Tell why your candidates should win the election. Make a bulletin-board display of the winning candidates.

7. Here are main ideas for the stories in this unit. Match each main idea with its story.

It was only fair that they were not put to death.  
They discovered that they liked to work.  
He made a bet and lost.  
It was afraid that it would be hurt again.

8. Here are some statements that characters in the stories or poems might have made about themselves. Match each statement with the character who might have said it.

I'm afraid of my shadow.  
We're as busy as beavers.  
I'm the world's best detective.  
I'd forget my head if it wasn't fastened on  
It's mainly a matter of being a smart cat.  
We're one big happy family.

# Some Books to Read

*Basil of Baker Street*, by Eve Titus.

This British mouse lives in the cellar of the famous house where Sherlock Holmes lived. Basil is a detective, too, and solves one of mousedom's most puzzling cases.

*The Borrowers*, by Mary Norton.

This family of tiny people, no taller than a pencil, live in the walls of a quiet old house and have many an adventure.

*Circus: April 1st*, by Louis Slobodkin.

When an elephant gets lost from the circus, almost anything can happen.

*Miss Pickerell Goes to Mars*, by Ellen MacGregor.

Miss Pickerell finds herself quite by mistake on a trip through outer space headed for the planet Mars.

*Pippi Longstocking*, by Astrid Lindgren.

Pippi lives alone except for her horse and pet monkey, but wherever she goes, amusing adventure goes with her.

*The Tough Winter*, by Robert Lawson.

The "Rabbit Hill" folk have a hard time when the dwellers in the big house go south for the winter.

# To the Rescue

# Little Vic

Little Vic's father and mother were both race horses, and so everyone thought that Little Vic would be one, too. He looked just like his famous father, even to the white star on his wide forehead. But even if he looked like a race horse, Little Vic didn't act like one. He was much too gentle to suit his trainer.

"I like to see a colt with more fight in him," the trainer would say when Little Vic came back to the stables after a workout. "His father was hard to work with, but nothing seems to trouble Little Vic."

"Little Vic's O.K.," the stable boy would say. "He's got more sense than all the other horses put together. Just you wait until he gets on the track. He'll show them a thing or two."

The stable boy loved Little Vic and believed in him.

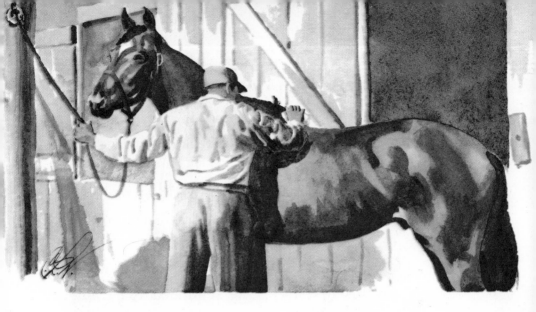

The day came at last for Little Vic's first real race. The stable boy rubbed him until his coat was shiny even in the shadows. Little Vic nipped him playfully on the shoulder as if to say, "Take it easy, boy. It's not so important as all that."

Everyone was much excited when Little Vic came dancing out on the track.

"He looks just like his father," they said. "He's the best looking colt of the bunch. He'll be a great race horse."

The horses lined up at the starting gate. Several of the colts were frisky and backed and jumped. Little Vic, however, stood very still and waited for the others to quiet down.

At last the barrier was lifted, and a shout went up from the crowd, "They're off!"

337

So they were—all but Little Vic. He still stood quietly. His head was lifted to where a silver airplane flew low over the track. He had never seen one before.

His rider did everything he could to make him start. Little Vic just went on watching the airplane, and the race was run without him.

The stable boy still believed in him, however. "It was his first race," he reminded the trainer. "He'll start all right the next time."

The next day Little Vic was again put into the race. Again he stood quietly, but this time his rider was ready for him. As soon as the barrier was lifted, he brought his stinging whip down sharply across Little Vic's sides.

Now Little Vic had sense enough to know that he had done nothing for which to get a whipping. It made him very angry. All the fire and life of his famous father came up in him. He forgot all about the race and wanted only to throw the mean rider off his back.

With a snort he whirled about and began to buck. He snorted and bucked as hard as a wild colt in a rodeo. He bucked so hard that his rider went sailing off into the air.

338

Back at the stable, his friend the stable boy said, "You were right to throw that rider. He isn't good enough to ride a horse like you."

Little Vic nibbled his feed and seemed very happy now about everything, but his owner was far from happy. This was the second time that Little Vic had not started in a race. The owner thought that he was no good as a race horse and decided to sell him.

A man from Arizona who had seen the race that day was willing to give a fair price for Little Vic. So the next day the stable boy said good-by to him, and Little Vic was shipped to Arizona.

The man who bought him was named Mr. George, and he lived on a huge cattle ranch. It was so big that a great cross-country highway ran right through it.

In many places this highway crossed small river beds. Most of the year these Arizona river beds were dry, but at times they were filled with water from storms in the mountains. A great stream of water rushed down so fast that sometimes people got caught in its path and were drowned.

These sudden rushing streams of water are called flash floods.

One evening Mr. George was riding Little Vic along the edge of one of the deep, dry beds.

Little Vic had become the favorite horse at the ranch. All the cowboys liked him. Mr. George rode no other horse. He didn't care that Little Vic could not run so fast as his famous father. He was sure and safe.

After a while they came to a car parked at the edge of the river bed. Down below, a party of tourists was gathered around a campfire.

"Hi, there," Mr. George called down to them. "You aren't planning to camp there, are you?"

"Oh, yes," they called back. "We're out of the wind down here."

"But it isn't safe," said Mr. George. "A mountain storm might send a flood along here before morning. You'd be caught and drowned."

The tourists laughed. "You're just trying to scare us because we're new to this country."

"You could camp in the old house you passed two miles back," Mr. George said, but the tourists did not move. At last he rode away and left them there. "It may not rain after all," he thought, glancing up at the sky.

He had gone about two miles beyond the camp, when Little Vic stopped with a snort. His sharp ears had caught a sound, and his nose had sniffed something new. Mr. George wondered what could have frightened his horse, and he smiled at Little Vic's pointing ears. It was likely just a coyote!

Then suddenly he heard the sound of rushing water. What he feared had happened. There had been a storm in the mountains, and now the flood was rushing down the dry river bed.

The tourists would not hear it in time to climb up to safety. They would all be drowned!

He and Little Vic must try to get to them ahead of the water. He whirled the horse around and bent low in the saddle.

Little Vic jumped forward just as a race horse should when the barrier is lifted before him. Then he went into his racing stride. No, not his stride after all. It was his father's stride, famous the world over for its might and speed.

Above the roar of the water Mr. George could hear the mighty pounding of Little Vic's hoofs. It was like the beat of music to his ears.

On and on went the horse, but on and on came the water. Its roar seemed louder now. Was this because the horse was tiring, and his stride was getting slower?

Mr. George glanced back, but in the dark he could see nothing. Once Little Vic hit a stone, and sparks shot out into the night, but still his long legs worked smoothly and swiftly.

Now, ahead of them, Mr. George could see a small light shining. He knew it was the campfire of the tourists. He said something to Little Vic and saw one of the horse's ears turn back to catch the words.

It seemed then that Little Vic flew through the night, so fast did he go, his hoofs hardly touching the earth. The wind whistled past Mr. George's ears. He knew that never in all the long story of racing had any horse ever turned in a better race than this. Little Vic's father could be proud of him after all.

At last they were close enough so that the pounding of horses' hoofs reached the ears of the tourists. Mr. George shouted. The people quickly climbed up the steep bank out of the river bed. By the time Little Vic raced past them, the last one had reached safety.

Now they could hear the roar of the water. In another minute it rushed past them, washing out the campfire and taking all the camping things along with it. The tourists didn't care. Because of Little Vic, they were safe and sound, and very, very thankful.

They crowded around the horse and his rider, but Little Vic wouldn't let them touch him. Like every winner after a race, he felt all on edge. He lifted his head proudly and looked out into the darkness. Mr. George reached down and smoothed his lovely neck.

344

"You're not a horse," he said, "you're a wonder! You could be a race horse all right, but you've got too much sense for that. You run your best only when there's a good reason for it. And you'll never have a better reason than you had tonight."

Little Vic lowered his head and reached around to nip playfully at Mr. George's boot. It seemed as if he could understand every word and, like all real heroes, wanted to turn attention away from himself.

*Doris Gates*

345

# The Birds That Saved
# the Harvest

## *Gulls to the Rescue*

About a hundred years ago the first settlers came to the Great Salt Lake valley. Because they had left stores far behind, they brought seeds with them from the East to grow their own grain for food.

The second year, when their grain was almost ready to gather, a frightening thing happened. Thousands upon thousands of crickets appeared. They were not the kind of cricket that hops about in our gardens. They were a kind of big black cricket that eats wheat, corn, and other grain.

They came hopping across the fields in moving black lines, eating everything before them. What could the farmers do? They saw their winter store of food vanishing. Unless it was saved, the people would go hungry and die.

346

Fiercely the settlers battled the crickets, killing thousands of them, but there were still thousands more of the hungry creatures.

Suddenly, as if by magic, a cloud appeared—a cloud of white wings.

Thousands of hungry gulls, that nested on islands in the Great Salt Lake, flew down upon the fields and began to gobble the crickets. In a little while every cricket had vanished. The grain had been saved.

The people gave thanks to God. And years later their grandsons built a monument to help everyone remember how the gulls saved the grain.

347

This monument, topped by the figures of two gulls, can be seen today in Salt Lake City. But even better than a monument is the law that people passed to protect the living gulls. It is during the nesting season that they need to be protected.

Colonies of these gulls nest on islands in the Great Salt Lake and other lakes of Utah. One of the colonies is found on Rock Island in Utah Lake. Men who study birds sometimes go there to learn more about gulls. If you live near Utah Lake and are interested in birds, you may someday visit that gull colony. There is no law against watching the birds if you do not hurt them.

## An Island Home

You will make your trip to Rock Island in a motor boat, as it is quite a distance from the shore. But don't speed too fast over the water, for Utah Lake is beautiful. Mountains look down upon it. and the water shades from green to blue.

Rock Island is a very small island, which has been made in an interesting way. Utah Lake is filled mostly by cold water which rushes down from the snow-covered mountains around it and partly by water which rushes up through the lake bed from springs deep within the earth. The water from these springs is full of a mineral which, through the years, has piled up until it has made an island. It is on the gray rock of this mineral island that the gulls have their nests.

349

The island is shaped very much like a gull. To the southwest and the northeast its wings are about three city blocks long from tip to tip. To the southeast it has a tail two blocks long. However, when the water of the lake is high, as it often is, this gull shape cannot be seen.

There is a line of trees along the part of the island that is shaped like the body of a gull. Little plants two feet high cover some of the rocks. The seeds for these plants have been blown here from shore, and sand and earth washed up from the lake have helped them to take root.

While you are still several miles away from Rock Island, you will see a few gulls, for they fly out to meet your boat. They soar high overhead, sometimes working their wings hard, sometimes gliding along on the wind. The gulls seem to glide on the air as easily as the boat sails on the waters of Utah Lake.

If you have brought along a lunch to eat on the way to the island, save some bread for the gulls. They are always hungry. As soon as you throw a piece of bread into the air, there is a wild rush of wings as the gulls try to catch it in the air or on the surface of the water.

350

If the piece of bread is very big, the gull cannot eat it all in one bite. So his fellows chase him, hoping he will drop it.

Since gulls do not like oranges, you can play a trick on them by throwing a piece of orange into the air.

First one gull catches the piece of orange in his yellow bill, while his fellows rush after him. When he finds out what it is, he drops his prize and flies up over the boat again. But right away another gull speeds down to the piece of orange and takes it away in his bill. Close after him rush more hungry gulls. This happens over and over again before the gulls seem to learn that it is a trick.

These gulls, like all lake and sea gulls, have long, narrow wings. Their wings stretch about three feet from tip to tip, and their bodies are just a little more than a third as long.

Their webbed feet make the gulls good swimmers, and their feathers keep their bodies dry. While they are flying high over the boat, their bodies seem all white, but when they come down closer, you can see that their backs are a soft gray. There are black markings near the tip of each wing.

At last the boat reaches the mineral island, and you find a place to dock. But all is not quiet as you step ashore, for the gulls do not welcome you. They fly about excitedly and cry out anxiously and loudly. They do not seem to like it that you have come. They stay high above their nests, looking down at you with hard, glassy eyes.

There are thousands of them. They fly wing to wing without touching each other. They dive, they circle, they glide, but still they keep out of each other's way, and out of your way.

352

# Nests and Baby Gulls

To see the eggs or the baby gulls in the nest, you set out toward the southwest end of the gull-shaped island. There many of the nests have been made, because that is the warmer, less windy side. But if your trip is late in June, most of the baby gulls will have hatched and left the nest.

Even though they cannot fly at all or even walk very well, still they can make their way over the rocks with their little webbed feet. You may even see some of them paddling about near the shore of the island, and you will have a chance to study the baby gulls close at hand.

Later they lose their first black-spotted baby feathers. The new fluffy feathers that stand out all over them make the baby gulls look even bigger than their parents.

You find the nests on the rocks very close together, but they do not look much like nests. Any little low place in the rocks that can keep an egg from rolling seems to have been used for a nest and lined with grass, sticks, fluff, or feathers. The parent gulls used whatever was at hand and could be carried to the spot.

In and around some nests there are not only feathers and fluff but even small shells and cherry stones. The parent gulls eat fish, bugs, worms, and nearly anything they can find. They must bring food to the island for their young. The cherry stones are from cherries they have got in orchards miles away.

At first you may not see any eggs, but at last you find a nest with two gray-brown eggs a little larger than a hen's egg. They are spotted a dark brown that is almost a purple.

Most gulls lay three eggs, and it may be that there were three in this nest and that one of them has hatched. A baby gull that you have seen may have come from this nest.

354

You are so interested in the study of the gulls that the day is gone before you know it, and you must be on your way home.

On the trip back, you watch the lake and the mountains and the sky as the sun goes down. The nearer mountains turn a deep purple, while those far away look light blue. Turquoise blue and deep blue fill the sky. The clouds turn yellow and orange and purple under the magic of coming night. A new moon high in the June sky looks like a little orange cloud itself.

And still the gulls are with you. Their strong white wings, lined with silver in the moonlight, make a rushing sound in the wind. For with night the wind has come, and the gray-green water is no longer quiet.

As the boat nears the dock, the gulls turn, one by one, like airplanes, and head back home.

When you get off the boat this June evening, you are feeling happy because of all the interesting and exciting things you have seen. And you feel good to remember the nesting place of these gulls that helped our early farmers save their grain and so earned their right to a safe home.

*Constance M. McCullough*

# John Hudson's Surprise

## *The Secret Plan*

"Boy!"

"Yes, sir?"

John Hudson stood on the ship's deck before the captain and tried to look him straight in the eye. It was not easy because John had done something he shouldn't, and the captain always saw through everyone.

356

"You left the ship yesterday," said the captain, "without asking leave." Captain Henry Hudson believed in coming right to the point even with his own son.

The boy swallowed. "Yes, sir. I did."

As the big man looked hard at the boy, the wide eyes in his gruff face became a little softer. Who would not be proud of a boy who stood and faced what he had done?

Captain Hudson was thoughtful for a minute. Then he said, "You know that I told the crew they must not leave the ship, don't you? It is for the crew's own good."

"Yes, sir," answered John.

For several minutes there was quiet. "Why did you go, boy?" asked the captain at last. "Don't you know that I have enough troubles without some more because of you?"

John nodded his head. How well he knew! He was only the cabin boy, but he had eyes and ears.

He knew that the crew did not like his father and had talked against him almost from the very day they had sailed from home.

357

Their ship, the *Half Moon*, had sailed ever to the north in the hope of discovering the northern way to India. Some huge pieces of ice had almost broken the tiny ship, but his father had got them safely away. And now they had come to this more southern point, still hoping to discover the waterway to India. It had turned out to be only a very wide river.

Yes, John knew about the troubles Captain Henry Hudson was having.

He nodded his head sadly. "I did not mean to make trouble, sir."

"Then what did you mean to do?"

The boy was quiet. He dared not answer. His father would think his adventure foolish. John himself began to wonder if, after all, maybe it was foolish. It had seemed such a wonderful idea yesterday!

"I cannot say, sir."

Captain Hudson spoke almost angrily. "You must know what a chance you take when you leave the ship. These Indians are all right as long as we keep them in their place and have the ship between us. For a boy to row ashore and go off into the woods alone is too daring."

358

It was not so much that he was angry about the boy's adventures as that he was upset because John had been in danger.

John said nothing. He just waited.

"You must learn to keep the rules," decided the captain. "It doesn't matter that you are my son. You must do as you are told."

"Yes, sir."

Captain Hudson thought about it for a while. His eyes looked across the sparkling bay in which they were anchored, and followed the line of the forest along the shore. All the trees had turned a bright red, and the water below them shone with the same color. No wonder the boy wanted to get into the woods, but that made no difference. He must learn to keep the rules.

Captain Hudson spoke gruffly. "Go to the cook. You are to stay under him, cleaning fish and washing pots until we lift anchor. You understand?"

"Yes—yes, sir," answered John.

His father knew that he could not have picked on anything that would be more unpleasant for the boy. He took it like a man, however, and turned to go.

359

"And, boy!" said Captain Hudson.

"Yes, sir?"

"Try not to be so much like me. It will keep you out of much danger."

John smiled and nodded. Then he went slowly to the cook, who was glad enough to have a little help. The cook set him at once to the cleaning of a huge fish which they were to have at noon.

John cleaned away with a will, but his thoughts were going round and round. He must think and plan, think and plan. Yesterday he had made a start on the plan. Today he must finish it.

What his father did not know was that he had not only seen Indians with bows and arrows the day before, but had talked with them.

They were boys no older than he, but they had something which John knew every one of the crew, even the captain himself, would give almost anything to have. John wanted to get it for them, for it was very important. It might even mean the difference between a happy crew on the way home or a very unhappy one.

How was he to get away? He thought about this all morning. He had to go to the Indians again. They were too afraid to come to him. He had no way of knowing they would keep their promise, but he must try to keep his.

The only thing he could think to do was to wait until evening. Then he would make believe he was tired from the day's work, and go to the stern deck for a little sleep.

The cook and the crew would laugh at him, but if luck were with him, everyone except the watchman would stay below decks talking. Then if he moved quietly, he could keep his promise to meet the Indian boys in the woods.

He thought it would never, never get dark. But at last the sun set, and John went about carrying out his plan. The air had a frosty nip in it as he got into a small boat and rowed away.

# A Good Trade

When his boat reached the shore of the bay, John was all out of breath from rowing hard, but just the same he raced for the meeting place.

Suppose the Indian boys hadn't waited for him! He stopped by the big spring. No one was in sight, but a deer and a raccoon watched from the underbrush.

His heart fell. He began to wish he had not come. It was so dark in the thick woods! The only sound was the lonely call of an owl.

362

Then the Indian boys appeared, slowly coming toward him out of the darkness.

As the Indians reached him, they began to talk by making signs with their hands.

Using signs is a very slow way to talk, and the Indians grew excited. Again and again John had to tell himself to take his time, for he was not going to let the boys get the better of him.

In the end he was successful. They had to give in. That made him feel very grown up.

The Indians even helped to carry the heavy baskets down to the water's edge and load them into the boat before he gave them his buttons. Then waving and shouting, they watched him row out into the bay.

John went swiftly toward the *Half Moon*, where he could see torches lighted on deck. Something must have happened while he was gone. He used all his might to row faster, until he was close to the great anchor cable.

363

"Is that you, boy?" a voice called sharply from the deck.

"Y-yes, sir," John answered.

He could see his father now, near the rail, shouting down at him, "Where have you been?"

John answered quickly. He was beginning to be afraid his adventure was not going to end as successfully as he had hoped.

"What is it you have there?" asked the captain.

"Chestnuts," said John, balancing himself as he stood up in the small boat.

"Chestnuts!" cried out Captain Hudson, reaching down to take a basket from John.

"Chestnuts!" shouted the men as they gathered to watch. "Chestnuts! Enough for us all?" they asked.

"Enough," said John, "and more. Twelve whole baskets full."

"Twelve!" said the captain. "How did you come by them?"

It was as though John had said he had a boatload of gold. The men could not have been more pleased. They were tired of living on hard bread and fish and wild game. Chestnuts would mean a feast to them. Even though they had had some of the sweet nuts up the river, it had not been enough. Now this boy had twelve whole baskets full!

"I traded them for my buttons," said John. "Two baskets for a button."

John thought his father would surely put him in irons and keep him there the rest of the trip. It was very quiet on deck as the men waited for Henry Hudson to speak.

At last he said, "It strikes me that we are both of us, boy, always wanting to do things full of danger. The only difference is that the things I do don't turn out so well as yours." Then he laughed.

Suddenly the unhappy feeling of the men changed. They said that even though Henry Hudson had failed to find the northern waterway to India, he had found something. He had discovered this big river where chestnuts grew. They even seemed proud of their captain now.

"John," said Captain Hudson.

"Yes, sir," said John, and he looked up at his father in the torch light. He was greatly surprised that his father should speak to him by name. Until now he had always been just "boy."

"Come up, John, and join me in the cabin."

As John followed his father to the cabin, he knew he was no longer a boy. He was John. He was John Hudson, a man, with a man's work behind him. And the crew were feeling merry. They would not make trouble on the long trip home.

*Mosser Mauger*

366

# Washington

He played by the river when he was young,
He raced with rabbits along the hills,
He fished for minnows, and climbed and swung,
And hooted back at the whippoorwills.
Strong and slender and tall he grew—
And then, one morning, the bugles blew.

Over the hills the summons came,
Over the river's shining rim.
He said that the bugles called his name,
He knew that his country needed him,
And he answered, "Coming!" and marched away
For many a night and many a day.

Perhaps when the marches were hot and long
He'd think of the river flowing by
Or, camping under the winter sky,
Would hear the whippoorwill's far-off song.
At work, at play, and in peace or strife,
He loved America all his life!

*Nancy Byrd Turner*

367

# Adventure at the Falls

## The Peddler's Cart

"I think it may rain, George," Mr. Messenger said to the boy beside him. "Most of the cows are lying down."

He had to raise his voice above the jingling of pots and pans that hung on the sides of the cart.

Every spring Mr. Messenger wheeled out the cart and gave it a fresh coat of paint. Then he loaded it with things that the farmers' wives wanted to buy. Pots and pans were hung on the outside. Their merry jingle would tell all the countryside that the peddler's cart was coming.

In this year of 1859 he had let George go with him along the roads of New York. George was ten and the youngest of the Messenger children.

Now they had sold most of the goods in the cart and were going to Buffalo to add to their supplies. The horses were picking their own way along the road. Mr. Messenger held the reins loosely and looked across the fields.

"This road was an Indian trail once," he said. "The Indians who lived hereabouts would come this way to trade their furs at Niagara."

368

"I've never seen an Indian," said George.

"Well, you're going to now," said his father, swinging the horses into a side road. "I've been wondering if we shouldn't go to the Indian reservation. What you've just said decides it."

The road they were following lay along the ridge of a hill looking down over flat country. Ahead of them at the side of the road a man was walking with a bundle of sticks on his back.

He did not turn until the noisy cart was beside him. Then he lifted his face toward the high seat and smiled.

Mr. Messenger stopped the horses.

"Well, well, Joseph," he said, "glad to see you! Glad to see you! Hop up with us. We're on our way to the reservation. This is my youngest, George. And this is Joseph Rain-Maker, George, one of my friends."

369

"You stay at our house when we get to reservation," Joseph said to them. "My wife will be very glad."

"Thank you, Joseph, if we won't be too much trouble," said Mr. Messenger.

Soon they came to the little house where they would spend the night. Mrs. Rain-Maker was there to welcome them with a smile.

The next morning she gave them breakfast in the kitchen. Then Joseph went out to help harness the horses.

"I go with you today," he said when the horses were harnessed.

"Why, that will be very nice, Joseph," said Mr. Messenger. "But how will you get back?"

"When the sun goes down, I will walk home," Joseph answered. "I get some willows for her baskets, and some May-apple roots for medicine in a place I know. She has had a dream. She wants me to stay with the boy today, as long as the sun is in the sky."

George looked up and saw Mrs. Rain-Maker standing in the doorway listening. Her friendly face showed no sign that she had heard what her husband had just said.

George felt a little shiver go down his back. Then he stuck his hands in his pockets and began to whistle.

"I'm not going to be scared. Dreams are silly," he thought.

All morning they drove past rich farms, along roads crowded with buggies and wagons. The people were friendly, the cattle fat, and trade went well for Mr. Messenger.

About noon they began to hear the roar of Niagara Falls. As they drove along the Gorge Road, George could see the river below them. Several times eagles flew across the deep gorge.

"Looking for things which come over the falls," his father said.

371

"But what would come over them?" George asked. "Wouldn't anything hear all that noise and keep away?"

Mr. Messenger shook his head.

"Mostly the creatures *do* understand," he said. "But sometimes an animal comes down to drink in the river just above the falls. Sometimes migrating birds settle where the water's running too swift, and can't rise again."

The falls themselves delighted George. He had never dreamed that so much water could be in such smooth motion at once.

"It's always the same picture, but never the same water," he shouted to his father. He had to shout to be heard above the roar of the falls.

They bought bread and cheese, which they ate on a grassy bank overlooking the falls. Joseph wouldn't let George go anywhere near the edge.

"We'd better make hay while the sun shines," Mr. Messenger said after lunch. "When we get near Buffalo, no one will pay even a nickel for a nice piece of ribbon. They like to get things from the stores."

Toward late afternoon they made their way once more to the river bank. Here, above the falls, the Niagara was wide and shallow. Along the shore there were stretches of flat dry rock that felt warm to George's bare feet. Across the river was another low shore, lined with willows.

On this side near the river were pine woods. This was where Joseph gathered his May-apple roots. In a place lying beyond the pines were more willows. They were the kind his wife needed for her baskets. It was so beautiful and peaceful that Mr. Messenger decided to unharness the horses and have supper there.

George went with Joseph to help him find May apples. His father would whistle when he was ready to start supper. Then George could gather a bundle of dry sticks for the campfire.

After a little while, George heard a whistle from the hill behind him. It was Mr. Messenger ready to get supper. George stopped looking for May apples and began to gather firewood.

Joseph had not yet filled the basket with roots when the whistle sounded again. George's arms were full, and he turned to go back to where his father stood. Joseph got up to join him.

"You needn't come with me," George said.

The Indian stopped and looked at the sun. It was almost touching the tops of the trees. All day nothing at all frightening had happened. The sun would be down in just a little while. Then all danger would be over.

"You stay with your father?" he asked.

"Sure," said George.

Slowly Joseph returned to his work, and George followed the trail through the trees. He came out to the shore where his father was waiting to build the fire.

When the fire was started, the two stood looking down at it for a while.

"I guess that'll catch now," Mr. Messenger said in a few minutes. "You stay here, George. I'll go back to the wagon and get the meat and things."

374

# The Migrating Swans

George watched his father walk away, then looked at the river. Suddenly he gave a shout and ran toward the edge of the water, waving his arms.

A flight of swans was coming down through the sunset air. Their feet were dropping down for their landing on the smooth water. George ran toward them, shouting and waving.

He was remembering what his father had told him about the migrating birds that settled on the water. Sometimes they were swept over the falls by the swift, whirling motion of the water before they could rise again, he had said.

"Shoo!" yelled George. "Shoo, shoo!"

Still the swans circled, coming nearer and nearer to the river.

Still George ran toward them. Behind him his father was shouting for him to come back. George could not hear those shouts above his own.

His bare feet had struck the water now. He was splashing in the shallow water, running down river along the edge. It felt cool to his feet, smooth and slippery and cool.

George yelled once more, louder than ever, and waved with all his might. The leader of the swans began to climb the stairways of the wind, followed by the others. Their great wings beat the air in flight. Their cries rang forth. George had frightened them away from their danger.

But where was the boy who had saved them? With his last shout, his last wild wave, George had lost his balance on the slippery stones.

The water was not much more than a foot deep, but it was very swift. As he tried to get to his feet, he again slipped and was carried away, choking and struggling. He saw his father running along the shore, trying to overtake him.

Fast as his father was coming, the river was faster still. George could not crawl from its hold. His hands reached helplessly for a hold on the smooth rocks as he struggled in the water.

He was more frightened than he had ever been in his life. He could think only of the falls toward which he was being pulled, faster and faster.

"Father!" he tried to shout. But his mouth was filled with water, and he was choking. Faster and faster he went. His father had lost his race with the river.

From the pines a little point of land ran out for a few yards into the water. The river circled past it. George was now too weak to work his way toward it.

It was on this point that Joseph Rain-Maker stood waiting, as quietly as an animal about to spring. He had heard George's shouts to the swans, and the yell which had followed.

Here was the danger he had been warned about! He had been careless. The sun was not quite down!

As he broke through the willows, Joseph saw the struggling boy and the running man. He turned and ran away from them. His best chance, he knew, was at the little point not far below him. If he missed George there, he would not be able to save him.

Now George was being swept toward him just as Joseph reached the little point of land. Kicking off his moccasins, he walked quickly into the water.

Up to his knees in the river, he reached for the body which was sweeping toward him. His hand caught at the shirt, but it slipped through his fingers. He tried once more. This time the brown fingers caught George's arm.

The boy's body stopped. Slowly the Indian pulled George toward him, until he could lift him from the river.

As he turned to make his way back to the shore, he saw that the sun had set.

It was Mr. Messenger now who took George out of Joseph's arms and carried him back to the fire. By the time they had reached it, George was able to speak.

"Let me down, Father. I'm too big."

He was ashamed of his adventure. He had been a silly-billy to fall down like that and make so much trouble for everyone. Had the migrating swans gone up river where they belonged?

George put on dry clothing while his father made some hot tea. As George was drinking the tea, he began to think about the adventure. It would be something to tell the family when they got home. He could hear them on winter evenings saying, "Tell us about the time you were almost carried over the falls, George."

There wasn't anybody else back home who had almost been carried over Niagara Falls, he'd bet a nickel!

*Elizabeth Coatsworth*

# The Meaning of the Word

## *A Golden Crop*

"Re-spon-si-bil-i-ty," Peter spelled slowly, his blue eyes tightly closed so he wouldn't see the open book in front of him.

It was a mouthful of a word all right, and there wasn't much chance that the teacher would get up to anything that size.

Still you never could tell. When there were only two or three people left in a spelling contest, she was likely to jump right out of the speller into words hard enough to knock you down. There would be no easy, nickel words tomorrow.

"Peter!" his mother called. "Your supper is getting cold."

Outside the window Peter could see Pa coming slowly up from the cornfield. Corn was the family's money crop.

Pa had planted eighty acres of it this year, and then everything had held the crop back . . . a wet spring, a cold summer, the slow-drying bottom land on which it grew. Not until late summer had there been bright sunshiny days and nights so hot and still you could fairly hear the leaves rustle as the ripening corn grew higher.

Now Pa was worried that it wouldn't dry enough before winter storms struck. The neighbors had all finished harvesting last week, but Pa's crop was slower.

The corn looked dry enough to Peter, its long rows golden and rustling, its dry leaves whispering, whispering like waves washing against a shore.

Thinking about the harvest, Peter got to his feet and went out to the warm kitchen where supper was spread. Dirk was putting away his second helping of squash.

"Pa is out looking at the clouds again," Ma said worriedly.

"There's a blizzard up in the north," said Dirk. "We're sure to get it."

"Ah, not with the corn still in the field!" Ma said anxiously and turned back to the stove.

Both boys knew what she was thinking. The big heavy ears of corn were good as gold to meet the bills, to buy the new furnace . . . but not while they hung in the field. If a blizzard came before they could be picked, the stalks would be blanketed with snow. It might well be spring before the field was again ready to pick.

Pa came in the back door, closing it behind him. "Tomorrow we harvest," he said flatly. "The corn is ready, and it is foolish to take any more chances on the weather. We will start with daylight."

"Tomorrow?" exclaimed Peter. "I can't miss school tomorrow. There's the spelling contest."

Pa looked at him sternly. "Dirk is all the man I need."

"But Dirk's got a debate," Peter choked and broke off, stopped by his brother's cold glare. Well, all right, he was just trying to help Dirk out! A debating team needed its captain, but if Dirk just didn't care—

382

Why was everybody silent as a clam, and down on him all at once? . . . Pa scowling, Dirk glaring, even Ma looking sad. Peter gobbled the last bite of cherry pie on his plate and hurried up to his room. Families could be sort of funny sometimes.

When Peter came down to breakfast the next morning, Pa and Dirk were out in the field. The air was frosty cold, the sky clear. Huh, thought Peter, no sign of the blizzard. Dirk could just as well not have missed his debate.

Peter ate steadily through his usual breakfast and was ready for the two-mile walk to school by eight o'clock. Might as well get started, he thought. Maybe he could brush up on a few more words before the contest.

"Responsibility," he said. "Re-spon-si-bil-i-ty." Yes, he still remembered it.

Peter waited on the doorstep, looking toward the field. Pa and Dirk were already at work. Dirk was unhitching a loaded wagon of corn from the picker. Pa was steering the tractor straight into the barnyard. Low on gasoline, Peter guessed.

A second later Pa put on the brake, skidded to a stop, leaped off, and was pulling out the hose from the big tank where gasoline was stored.

"Hey, Pa!" called Peter. "Pa, you didn't turn off your engine!"

Faster than the words, it happened. One second there was Pa holding the hose. The next second he was hidden by flames, as if by a red curtain. Gasoline had run over the hot machine and caught on fire.

384

Peter started to run toward his father, but it seemed to take him seven years to move a step. He could see Dirk running, Pa's hand coming through the flames, slinging the hose away, turning off the engine.

Suddenly it was over. The last sparks died down along the trail of gasoline drops from the hose lying on the ground. Dirk was off to the house for oil and a bundle of soft cotton cloths. Ma was gently taking care of Pa's burned arms.

"I must take you to the hospital," she said to Pa, helping him into the car. And to the boys, "He'll be all right. Don't worry." Then she put the car in gear and backed it out of the garage.

Dirk stepped close to the car. "We'll stick by the corn, Pa," he said, his voice very steady. "We'll get it in all right. Won't we, Peter?"

"Sure," Peter said. "Sure, we'll manage, Pa."

He saw Pa's eyes shining back at them, warmly, proudly, as the car moved down the drive.

"Let's get started, Peter," Dirk said. His voice was gentle, not a bit bossy. "I'll take the corn picker. You run the tractor."

Driving carefully, Peter chugged back to the cornfield. This was a man's work, and he'd do it well. Every bushel harvested would help.

As the morning hours went by, Peter's eagerness wore off. An aching tiredness took its place. The sun climbed higher and burned the back of his neck. Every inch of his body seemed to be aching. He was very hungry, too, but the noon hour brought only more work.

Why hadn't Ma come back from the hospital? Was Pa badly burned?

386

## A Race against Time

Dirk glanced at the sky from time to time. Peter looked, too. There was nothing to see but a cloud to the north that he could cover with his hand. Peter gave a weary sigh and looked at the cloud again.

"Hey, Dirk!" he called uneasily. "It's getting bigger!"

"Be here by dark," Dirk said.

Peter glared at the untouched acres of corn. "Dirk, we can't finish it!" he exclaimed.

"No," Dirk answered, not stopping, "but we'll get every bushel we can."

Silently Peter settled down to help, bending his aching shoulders over the work.

It was a losing battle, and he was ready to cry with weariness, but he managed to keep going. Every ear of corn counted toward a bushel.

Suddenly he straightened up and stared unbelievingly at the road that ran past their farm. What crazy kind of circus parade was coming? It looked like a long, crawling worm with giraffe heads shooting up every few feet! It bobbed and swayed and turned in at the gate!

At the edge of the field Dirk gave a great shout and stopped the picker. "Peter, they're coming to help us—all the neighbors! Seven, eight, nine corn pickers! More than twenty-four tractors and wagons!"

The parade came rolling up around them. Mr. Hill rode the lead picker, Mr. White the second, and Mr. Temple was third. All the other neighbors for miles around followed behind them.

"Heard about your Pa's bad luck," Mr. Hill said kindly. "The boys here thought we'd better give you a hand." He stared out over the harvested acres. "You did all this? You have really been working!"

388

"Peter helped a lot," Dirk said.

"Yes, I can see that," Mr. Hill said. "Guess there's enough of us to do the work now. Why don't you knock off and rest, Peter? You've done a man's job today."

Thankfully, Peter walked toward the back steps while nine corn pickers, Dirk's making ten, swept into the waiting rows of rustling corn with a mighty roar. Peter felt a big lump welling in his throat at the sight. It was no longer a losing battle. Let the cloud grow now, let the blizzard come . . . the eighty acres of corn would be harvested before dark!

389

A man's job! That's what he'd done. For six long aching hours he'd been grown up, and he'd found out what it could mean. Not a thing more or less than that long word he'd mastered yesterday . . . re-spon-si-bil-i-ty.

He'd missed the spelling contest, and Dirk his debate, because they felt responsibility for their family. All these men had left their own work because they felt responsibility for their neighbors.

The old car rumbled into the driveway, and Ma hopped out, her face tired but shining.

"Pa's fine!" she called happily to Peter. "I stayed until he was feeling better. They'll let him come home in no time. And oh, Peter, the neighbors came, didn't they? I'll get some coffee for them right away." Then she hurried off.

Peter's eyes went from Dirk still in the field to his mother hurrying to the kitchen and he sighed a little. He knew now that once you let a big word like *responsibility* get into your head, you couldn't ever quite get it out again.

"Ma," Peter called, trailing her into the kitchen, "You want any work done?"

*Nan Gilbert*

# A Nation's Strength

Not gold, but only man can make
  A people great and strong;
Men who, for truth and honor's sake,
  Stand fast and suffer long.

Brave men who work while others sleep,
  Who dare while others fly—
They build a nation's pillars deep
  And lift them to the sky.

*Ralph Waldo Emerson*

391

# Things to Think About and Do

1. Look through the stories for clues to the time of year when each took place. Then make a chart of the seasons and stories. Under the right season on your chart write the name of the story and the sentence that gave you your clue.

2. Sometimes little things in a story tell much about the characters: where they lived, when they lived, if they were rich or poor. Be ready to explain what the clues to the right of the people listed below tell you about those people.

| | |
|---|---|
| The Messengers | peddler's cart |
| Peter's family | eighty acres of corn |
| Little Vic's owner | a huge cattle ranch |
| Henry Hudson | the northern way to India |
| Joseph | Indian reservation |
| Utah settlers | left cities far behind |

3. With two others in your group act out the meetings that John Hudson had with the Indian boys. How did they make one another understood since the Indians spoke no English?

4. What problems did characters in the stories of this unit have to face? Which one took the greatest responsibility in meeting his problem? Be ready to tell why you think so.

5. If a swarm of crickets were to attack the crops in Utah now, what could be done to fight them? Write a modern story of the crickets and the western farmers.

6. Look up the word *hero* in your dictionary. Make a list of the things we think about when we describe a hero. Talk with the group about your idea of a hero. What famous living person is the class hero?

7. Each of the following things was important in one of the stories. Tell which story each one was in and why it was important.

<table>
<tr><td>a fire</td><td>chestnuts</td><td>migrating swans</td></tr>
<tr><td></td><td>a flash flood</td><td>black crickets</td></tr>
</table>

8. Work with a friend and look up one of the following headings in an encyclopedia or other books.

*Arizona*—in order to give a talk describing the country that the tourists would have seen.

*Horses*—in order to give a talk about the work Little Vic would have done if he had been a cow pony instead of a race horse.

*Ships*—in order to give a talk about the ships that sailed the seas in the days of the *Half Moon*.

*Corn Belt*—in order to give a talk about the farm where Peter and his family lived.

# Some Books to Read

*The Cave*, by Elizabeth Coatsworth.

An Indian boy who herds sheep turns fear of a ghost cave into a life-saving use.

*The Corn Grows Ripe*, by Dorothy Rhoads.

Tigre, a boy of Yucatan, learns to be patient as he works at a man's job.

*Little Vic*, by Doris Gates.

The white-starred colt was born on a Kentucky farm where Pony Rivers worked. And Pony knew at once that someday Little Vic would be a great horse.

*Maggie Rose*, by Ruth Sawyer.

A plucky girl finds a way to help her family in time of trouble.

*The Peddler's Cart*, by Elizabeth Coatsworth.

This is the lively book from which came the story "Adventure at the Falls."

*The Secret Horse*, by Marion Holland.

Nickie and Gail set out to "save" the horse at the animal shelter. Their problems are many, all complicated by a big brother and a very nosey little one.

*Use Your Head, Hildy*, by May Justus.

Surprising things happen when Hildy is left in charge of the family while her mother is away.

# Neighbors

# Round the World

# Maps

High adventure
  And bright dream—
Maps are mightier
  Than they seem:

Ships that follow
  Leaning stars—
Red and gold of
  Strange bazaars—

Ice floes hid
  Beyond all knowing—
Planes that ride where
  Winds are blowing!

Train maps, maps of
  Wind and weather,
Road maps—taken
  Altogether

Maps are really
  Magic wands
For home-staying
  Vagabonds!

*Dorothy Brown Thompson*

# The First Lamb

## *Shepherd Boys*

His name was Abd el Karuzeh. His father and his mother said it deep down in their throats so that each part of it sounded almost the same as all the others, like the echo of little stones dropped into a deep well.

It was a big name for a small boy, but he was older than he looked. All the people who live in the caves in the hill country of North Africa are small people.

Abd el Karuzeh was ten years old, and for two years now he had helped herd the village flocks.

Every morning Abd el Karuzeh and the other young boys went from cave to cave and called out the sheep and goats of the family or families living there.

Then uphill they all went, following trails which only they could see, and climbing hills and crags which only sheep and goats and boys of the mountain country could climb.

397

One by one Abd el Karuzeh and the other boys rounded up a dozen or more ewes with their lambs. Each boy with his flock stopped on some hillside where the sun had brought a little green out of the earth. Sheep are stupid creatures, Abd el Karuzeh's father said, and there has to be much food under their very noses—else they will die!

Farther on, among the rocks, the bigger boys kept the goats.

Still farther, among the crags where one could see hardly any green thing, the boys who were almost men helped the camels to find a little food. They did not come back to the caves every night. Each of those older boys carried a spear, for no one knew when a lion would spring from a rock.

Abd el Karuzeh carried a sharp, pointed knife stuck through his belt, but lions did not often come close to the caves. He had only hyenas to be afraid of—and then only after dark.

Darkness comes quickly in the mountains, once the sun has set. Well Abd el Karuzeh knew that when the shadows of the rocks began to grow blue, he must gather his ewes and their lambs together and hurry down the hill. The sheep made a light sound on the rocks, but a hyena made no sound at all until its strong teeth had broken a lamb's neck.

Abd el Karuzeh was not thinking of hyenas on this sunny afternoon. He was sitting on a huge rock and feeling sorry for himself.

Abd el Karuzeh's father was poor—poor even for the people who lived in the caves of North Africa. He owned only a half-dozen sheep. Therefore he had not, like other fathers, given his son a lamb with which to start a flock of his own.

"You must earn your first lamb," he had answered when the boy asked. He had turned his face away when he said it, for he loved his son and it was hard to tell him this.

How was any boy to start a flock without even one lamb to call his own? Abd el Karuzeh sat on the ledge of rock, swinging his feet against its warm sides as he thought.

What could he do to earn a lamb? He asked himself this question hundreds of times, but there was no answer.

Just then Abd el Karuzeh heard a shout, and he looked up to see another shepherd. The sun was already red in the western sky, and the shepherds were rounding up their flocks to return to the caves. Abd el Karuzeh, being one of the youngest boys, did not go as far into the hills as the others, so he waited as they brought down their sheep.

400

# A Lamb Left Behind

The sun fell lower and lower until the highest crags hid part of it.

"The Headman's sons are late," one shepherd said uneasily, looking up at the hills.

"Do you see them, Abd el Karuzeh?" asked another. "Your eyes are sharp."

Abd el Karuzeh looked across the hillsides, but there was no sign of the two boys and their flock.

The other boys stood waiting for the sons of the Headman. They would have waited for any one of the shepherds, even the poorest. No shepherd boy leaves another alone in the hills after dark, for even men are afraid of the hyena at night.

Where were Feragi and Fuad? Even the sheep and goats bunched together as though afraid.

What was that? It sounded like the patter of rain on dry leaves. A sigh of relief broke from the boys, and the flock started milling about as though glad. Hurrying down the path, their feet scattering stones, came the Headman's sons and their sheep, but they were not happy boys.

"We have had to leave a lamb," said Fuad, the older of the two.

The boys' relief turned to sadness. Not only are his sheep of use to a shepherd, but he loves them as a mother loves a baby. Just as no careful mother will leave her baby, so a good shepherd will not abandon one of his flock in the hills.

"What happened?" asked someone in a low voice, and every boy bent forward, listening for the answer to this question.

"She-of-the-Quick-Light-Feet went off a little way from the flock," Fuad said, "and I followed to bring her back. When I was but two or three steps from her, I saw a snake among the stones between us, and I threw a rock at it. I killed the snake, but our ewe, She-of-the-Quick-Light-Feet, was frightened and leaped sideways, knocking one of her twin lambs over the cliff."

"Could you not reach it?" Abd el Karuzeh knew the answer to that question before he asked.

"No," Fuad said. "It fell on a narrow ledge that stuck out from the cliff. If we could have got down to it, we could not have climbed back up again. It is a pity, too."

"And it was unhurt," Feragi added.

402

"It will be hurt soon," Fuad said shortly, as he
started his friends and the animals down the trail.
"Even now a hyena may have it. Oh, we tried to
get it, but rocks snapped under our hands, and
bushes broke under our weight."

"A lamb, a fine lamb, alive and unhurt, where
a boy might reach it," thought Abd el Karuzeh.
It seemed a pity to abandon it to the hyenas.

"*Yah hya ris!* Yes, my captain!"

The shepherds were singing as they always did
when marching home at night.

They did not see that Abd el Karuzeh had stayed behind them. He stopped short. Back there in the dim evening light was a lamb, a good lamb, unhurt—on a ledge where he might rescue it. Back there, too, there might be hyenas ready to kill a lamb or a boy!

"*Yah hya ris!*" came the shepherds' song. That way lay food, the warm caves, friends, safety. As Abd el Karuzeh looked after the boys, he saw Fuad go over to a tired lamb, pick it up, and swing it around his neck. He was a good shepherd. He would never have abandoned a lamb if he could have reached it at all.

Suddenly Abd el Karuzeh turned and marched off into the darkness. One by one the stars came out, and the moon shone round and full as a yellow balloon.

"*Yah hya ris!*"

Abd el Karuzeh found himself singing softly as he hurried along. Thinking of the song helped him to forget about hyenas. When he sang, he could not hear what might run up behind him.

A stone rolled down the hillside, and he began to run much faster. Was there really something following him? He dared not look.

On and on he ran, with his heart in his throat and his blood pounding in his ears. His foot sent another stone downhill, and he thought he heard something bleating. He listened hard.

"Baaaaaaaah! Baaaaaaaah!"

Only a lamb—a cold lamb—bleated like that!

He followed the sad bleating call. Here was the place where Fuad and Feragi had dug their feet into the earth as they tried to climb down. And there, looking up at him, was the lamb!

Abd el Karuzeh took off his coat. He lay down flat, slid over the cliff, and with his foot felt for a place to stand. His fingers gripped the edge.

Inch by inch the boy crept down, holding hard to the rock in front of him. Time after time the rock beneath one foot or the other broke and went crashing down the mountainside into a canyon far below. Only his strong fingers saved him. Fuad had been right. The bushes were too small and the rock too easily broken to have held a larger boy. But this was no time to be discouraged.

At last he stood on the narrow ledge beside the lamb. With both pity and relief he picked it up, and it put its head against his shoulder. As he felt its warm wool, he could see in the dim moonlight that there was something dark on its back, and he saw, too, that his fingers were bleeding.

Savage beasts can smell blood a long way off. Abd el Karuzeh moved back against the cliff and peered to the right and left of him. There was no time to lose. The smell of blood would surely bring a wild beast, and quickly.

He put the lamb about his neck as he had seen Fuad do, took off his belt, and tied its feet together.

Climbing down the cliff had been slow, hard work. Climbing up was even slower and harder.

He was tired. His bleeding fingers hurt. The feet of the lamb about his neck hit the rock. He could not put his forehead as close to the cliff as he wanted to for safety. If the lamb should grow afraid and try to move, even a little, he might lose his balance. Then both would be thrown into the dark gorge beneath him.

There might be a hyena jumping savagely at his feet, or one waiting above to attack him. It seemed forever before his hands reached the flat rock and he crawled up over the top. Picking up his coat, he slung it over his arm and peered about.

407

Abd el Karuzeh was not quite sure how far he
was from his father's cave. He peered down the
long path he must take, and his breath caught in
his throat. A gleam of light! Was it a hyena's
eyes or those of some other savage beast? Now
a second and a third, then many gleams! What
animals were these?

He laughed aloud. Animals' eyes are in pairs,
and they are still in the darkness. Each of these
lights bobbed up and down in its own way.
Hyenas walk softly, too, and Abd el Karuzeh's
good ears caught the sound of footsteps almost as
soon as he had seen the torches.

"Halloooooo!" he shouted, pulling the last sound
out long and high.

"Halloooooo!" came back his father's voice. The
rocks rattled beneath his feet as he scampered
down the path, but there was no need to go
quietly now. No animal, however hungry or
savage, attacks men with fire in their hands.

Fuad and Feragi and their father were with the
group of men. Therefore Abd el Karuzeh untied
the lamb and placed it in Fuad's hands.

"Why do you do that, Abd el Karuzeh?" the
Headman asked.

"Did not your boys tell you?" Abd el Karuzeh asked in surprise. "It belongs to you. It is the lamb of your ewe, She-of-the-Quick-Light-Feet."

"It is a lamb my lads left to die," the Headman answered slowly. "Therefore it no longer belongs to us. We could not use its wool with gladness. When it was grown, we could not feel that its lambs were ours." The Headman turned to his son. "Fuad, return the lamb to its owner." And the boy obeyed.

Tears fell from Abd el Karuzeh's eyes and sank into the lamb's soft wool. It was not manly to cry, he knew, but now not only his fingers hurt, but his heart was very thankful.

"Abd el Karuzeh!" His father spoke sharply, as poor men the world over often do when they are proud of their children. The boy sank respectfully on one knee before the Headman and laid his forehead upon the Headman's hand in sign of thanks.

Then, with Fuad at one side and Feragi on the other, and his lamb—his very own lamb—in his arms, Abd el Karuzeh followed the group back to the safety and peace of the warm caves.

*Louise Stinetorf*

# Lars and the Wolves

## *On the March*

It was breakfast time in the Turi tent. Though it should have been day, moonlight lay bright upon the snow. The Turi tent was pitched in a snowy valley inside the Arctic Circle.

For a long time this Lapp family had been on the march, driving their reindeer herd to fresh grazing lands. Little by little, as the reindeer had eaten the moss hidden under the snow, they had moved on to fresher pastures.

410

Suddenly Tomos, one of the Turi sons, came into the tent. He had been with the reindeer all night and looked both tired and troubled.

Mother Turi hurried to bring him hot coffee, porridge, and pancakes. "Eat and drink, Tomos," she said gently. "Warm yourself, and then tell us your news. I fear something bad has happened. Your face says so."

Tomos sat down heavily and began to eat. After a minute he looked up from his porridge. "Wolves came to the herd," he said sadly.

Father Turi's eyes grew hard. "How many did they get?"

"Seven were cut off from the herd and killed," said Tomos.

Ten-year-old Lars gasped. Seven reindeer gone! This was very bad. Lapps couldn't live without their reindeer. Their porridge was made from dried reindeer milk. They ate dried reindeer meat on the long marches. Reindeer hide was used for their clothes, their tents, their lassoes. Reindeer even pulled their sleds. Now seven of the Turi herd were gone!

"I shall warn our neighbors," Mother Turi said quietly as Tomos lay down to sleep.

Other herds were spread through the valley. Some of them were from the Turi family's own village.

Now Mother Turi strapped the baby to her back and set off on her skis, a ski stick in one hand and a club in the other.

Father Turi turned to his son. "We must go at once to help with the herd. The wolves may return at any time. We shall be needed."

Lars was happy to be able to help if the wolves returned. He felt very proud as his father handed him a gun. Lars slung it over his shoulder. Just then there was a sudden barking from the dogs outside the tent.

Lars and his father hurried outside. A black speck was speeding toward them over the snow. It was a woman with a club, skiing.

"Wolves! Wolves!" she gasped, sliding to a stop. "Wolves have come!"

412

"Where? When? Has your herd, too, been attacked?" Father Turi cried.

"No, but it soon will be. The tracks of three packs have been seen," the woman said.

Quickly Father told what had happened to his own herd and of Mother's trip to warn the camps down the valley. "Move your camp nearer to us," Father said, "and we shall fight the wolves together."

The woman turned to speed back toward her own camp.

Lars and his father then returned to the tent. They filled their pockets with reindeer meat and pancakes. Father slung a gun over his shoulder, and each fastened a club to his belt. Then picking up their lassoes and followed by half a dozen dogs, they skied away to the herd.

413

When they reached the herd, they found the reindeer moving about. Their eyes were wild and full of fear. The herders and their dogs were circling the reindeer, trying to keep the animals together.

"No wolves have come back," one of the men shouted to Father. "They struck during the night and then disappeared over the hill."

Father skied toward the mountain, hoping to track down the wolves. Lars and the others stayed to watch the herd. They circled the reindeer, trying to keep the frightened animals together and to quiet them.

414

In the afternoon Father returned. The wolves had gone and could not be tracked. The herd must be moved nearer to camp. Now the watchers began shouting and waving their arms, and the dogs barked and rushed at the reindeer to start them moving toward camp.

Just then Tomos appeared on his skis. Mother was home, he said, and two herds had already moved into the valley.

That night everybody from the Turi tent went out to watch the reindeer. Everyone knew that the wolves were only hiding and soon would strike again. The reindeer were still restless. They had stopped grazing. No noses were digging for moss under the snow. The dogs, too, were excited and howled and barked and held their noses to the air, trying to get the wolf scent.

415

All night long the people circled the herds. Lars was proud this year to be in the outer circle with the men. No wolf was seen that night.

Next morning all the Turis except Father and Tomos skied back to their tent for coffee and reindeer meat and sleep. Father and Tomos could catch short naps standing up on their skis, leaning on ski sticks. Brush fires were built in a great circle around the herd to scare away the wolves while the men took their naps.

There was not enough moss left in the valley to keep so many animals here much longer. The wolves must be hunted down before the reindeer could graze again under the snow in better pastures. Today was a day of waiting for the enemy to come out of its hiding place.

It began to snow. It snowed almost all day. There was great fear that the wolves might strike during the snowstorm. Late in the day the snow stopped, and the wolf hunt was planned.

416

# The Wolf Hunt

Lars wondered if he would be allowed to go, and sure enough he was. Leaving the women to protect the herd, Father Turi set out with Lars and Tomos.

They looked in every direction through the moonlight of the arctic day. As far as they could see, the snow lay smooth without a track upon it. Lars's eyes were bright and eager now.

"Today, when the wolves come out of hiding, Lars shall get his first wolf!" he said.

Father Turi made no answer. Tomos, too, was silent. Their eyes were watching a black speck far across the white plain below them. The speck grew larger. Wolves! A wolf pack was moving toward them and toward the reindeer herd behind them.

"The wind blows from us to them," Father grumbled. "They know where we are and where the herd is."

Suddenly he flew down the hillside like the wind, with Tomos and Lars close behind, heading for the wolf pack.

417

Lars's heart beat faster. These wolves must be very hungry, or they would have turned back at the scent of man. He thought of wolf stories that had been told to him. The leaders of the wolf packs were clever in planning their attacks.

Now the wind changed. Instead of blowing at Lars's back, it was in his face. Lars's white teeth gleamed in a smile. Luck was with the hunters now. The wolves would no longer sniff the human scent, or know how close the hunters were. Lars followed in Father Turi's ski tracks, half circling the plain across which the wolf pack trotted.

There were about thirty wolves coming through the snow with the chief of the pack leading, some distance ahead of the others. The chief was bigger and darker than any wolf in the pack.

Suddenly the wolf leader stood still, and the pack divided into two parts.

418

The new pack, following a new chief, turned
to circle the hill down which Lars had skied. It
was heading for the forest behind it, the forest
in which the huge reindeer herd was gathered.
The pack behind the old chief stayed where it
was. Lars saw that the new pack was planning
to drive the reindeer toward the others.

"Tomos," ordered Father quickly, "return to
the herd and tell the watchers that the wolves
have divided and that one part is circling the hill
behind them. Stay to help protect the reindeer."

Lars and his father watched from behind a
great rock, guns in hand. The Turi dogs stayed
close to their masters. They were wise in the way
of wolves!

419

Suddenly the old chief started forward and his pack followed. Together Lars and his father fired into the pack, and two wolves fell. Quickly they skied after the running wolves.

The frightened reindeer herd was in sight, swept toward them by the second wolf pack. The Turis could not fire again in that direction for fear of wounding the watchers or their dogs.

Now Lars whirled his lasso above his head. He shouted with delight when it fell about the neck and shoulders of a big wolf. As the lasso tightened, the animal rolled over and over in the snow. Lars ended its life with his knife. He had killed his first wolf!

Now the reindeer herd was here, moving through the snow into the very mouths of the wolves. Two wolves together leaped toward a reindeer, to pull it down. Father clubbed one, while a dog jumped at the other. Before the wolf could turn upon the dog, the reindeer, a large one, drove the wolf into the snow with its great horns. The wolf did not move again.

All around, on every side, men and wolves and dogs were fighting. The noise of the battle filled the forest.

420

All at once, as if they had been given a signal, the wolves turned and ran. Each disappeared in his own direction. The Lapps did not try to follow them. Their work now was to quiet the reindeer and get the herds of three families straightened out. The reindeer of each family were known by that family's mark on the ears.

Lars counted the wolves that had been killed during the battle. There were twenty in all to be skinned for their fur.

Once more at home in the tent, before having his first real sleep in two days and nights, Father Turi put an arm across Lars's shoulders.

"My son did a man's work today," he said proudly.

*Faith Y. Knoop*

# The Fisherman

Fisher, in your bright bark rowing,
Whither fishing are you going?
   All is lovely, all is lovely,
   All is lovely, fisherman.

See you not that last star hiding
In a cloud, as you are riding?
   Take your sail in, take your sail in,
   Take your sail in, fisherman.

If your net you are entangling,
Sail and oar soon will be dangling.
   O be wary, O be wary,
   O be wary, fisherman.

Danger lurks for him who listens
Where the singing mermaid glistens,
    Gaze not on her, gaze not on her,
    Gaze not on her, fisherman.

Fisher, in your bright bark rowing,
Turn your prow, you'd best be going,
    Flee from danger, flee from danger,
    Flee from danger, fisherman.

*Anne Higginson Spicer*
(*From a Portuguese folk poem*)

# Wings to the North!

## Off by Dog Sled

Alec was eating a late breakfast. Usually it didn't matter when he got up. At this time of year the sun shone for twenty hours of the day. There was time enough to do everything that had to be done, and there was no school.

Mr. Evans, the teacher, had been away for three weeks. He was visiting the Eskimos and their sealing camp beside the open water far out on the ice-covered sea.

"Nanook and I are going to pick up a cache of meat when the wind dies down," Alec told his mother, as he poured canned milk over his bowl of rice.

424

Nanook was an Eskimo boy and Alec's best friend.

"What dogs are you going to take?" Mrs. Sutherland asked. "Isn't Nanook's father still at the sealing camp along the coast?"

Nanook and Alec often took the Eskimo's dogs whenever Nanook's father was at the Post.

"We're going to take our pups," Alec said, looking out of the window. "My three and two of Nanook's—the biggest ones."

Out of the window Alec could see the base with its store and radio tower and a place for storing things. Beyond that group of buildings was the Royal Canadian Mounted Police Post.

425

When he had finished breakfast, Alec hurried to do his morning jobs around the house. Then he went over to the company store. There he found Nanook waiting for him. Behind the long counter Alec's father was working at his bookkeeping. He was the manager for the Northern Trading Company, as well as the weatherman at Stringer Inlet.

"Nanook tells me you're going to the cache today," Mr. Sutherland said, looking up from his work.

"Yes," Alec answered eagerly. "We're going to take the pups."

"Mm-m," said Mr. Sutherland. "Can they pull? Will you be back today?"

"Of course," said Alec. "It's only six miles there and back."

426

"You'd better take some supplies," said Mr. Sutherland. "Might as well make it a real trip. Why not take along the little oil stove to warm your beans?"

The boys liked the idea. It would be fun to turn this into a real trip and cook their dinner on the trail. Why, they'd be just like the Mounties on patrol!

They loaded the sled with their supplies, and covered it with a caribou skin. Then they hitched the pups to it and put on warm mittens. The pups were excited and playful. Alec and Nanook had all they could do to make them line up for the starting signal.

When it came, the team rushed off, pulling for dear life. Mr. Sutherland laughed to watch the lively take-off, the boys trotting alongside the sled, its steel runners squeaking on the hard snow.

Their course lay along the coast as far as Fram Point, then inland a couple of miles to the cache. Nanook's father had shot a caribou in the fall and had stored the meat away under a pile of rocks.

As the boys got under way, they heard the barking of dogs and saw another dog team starting off from the Post, with two men and a loaded sled.

Alec was surprised. "It's the Mounties!" he cried. "They are going on a patrol up the coast. I thought they had left!"

The boys raced along beside the team of the Royal Canadian Mounted Police as far as Fram Point. Then waving good-by to the Mounties, Alec and Nanook turned their team inland toward the cache.

There was no wind now, and the dogs had easy pulling over the frozen snow of the plain. Sometimes the boys rode on the sled. Sometimes they ran alongside it. The snow had softened in a few places, and the sled runners sinking into it made shallow ridges.

# From Dog Sled to Plane

The boys were still half a mile from the cache when all at once Alec thought he heard something. Then he was sure of it. He shouted across to Nanook, who stopped the dogs and made them lie down by sharply cracking the whip in the air.

"What is it?" he asked.

"A plane!" cried Alec. "Listen!"

The roar of the airplane was growing louder now, and the two boys stood looking up at the bright sky.

"There it is!" shouted Nanook. Alec saw it, too, flying in low from the west.

The plane passed above them and circled over the Post, then turned back inland again.

"It's coming down on the lake!" cried Nanook.

"Let's go over and watch it land," said Alec.

They turned the dogs and raced south toward a small lake where the ice was smooth.

When the boys reached the lake, the plane was down and the pilot busy unloading bags of mail and cartons of supplies on the snow.

"It's Nick Worth, I think," said Alec, reading the letters painted on the tail of the plane.

It was Nick all right, and he called to them, "Hi, boys! You didn't lose any time getting here. Can you help me take these cartons and mailbags to the Post?"

"We were on our way to a cache, but we can go there tomorrow," said Alec as he and Nanook began to load the cartons on the sled.

"I saw a dog team offshore as I flew over the Post," said Nick.

"That must have been the Mounties. They went off on a patrol up the coast. We raced them as far as Fram Point."

"No, they weren't near Fram Point. They were coming in from the sea," Nick said.

"That'll be my father and Mr. Evans," said Nanook, "coming in from the sealing camp."

They had almost reached a little ridge behind the Post when they saw a dog team coming out toward them from the Post. The two men who ran beside the sled turned out to be Mr. Sutherland and Mr. Evans. Kootawuk, Nanook's father, was not with them.

Mr. Evans hurried forward to meet Nick Worth. He looked worried.

"Sickness has broken out at the sealing camps. Several of the Eskimos are sick, and I'm afraid others will be. Kootawuk is not feeling well, so I brought him back with me. I've already left him at his house."

Alec's father broke in, "Nick, I radioed to see if Port Radium would send out a doctor. They said he would be ready if you would go back and pick him up."

"Do you think you could fly back to Port Radium and bring him out today?" asked Mr. Evans.

"Of course," said Nick. "We can make it easily. Will you come back with me to Port Radium—or maybe the boys would like to come?"

"Take the boys along. I have some other things to do, and I must take a package of medicine over to Kootawuk. You needn't worry about him, Nanook. He isn't very sick, just a sneezy cold, but I'm worried about the condition of the others if the doctor doesn't get here soon."

Later, whenever Alec thought about that day, it seemed more like a dream than something that had really happened.

Father had taken Nick and the boys back to the plane, and Mr. Evans had returned to the Post with the pups and their loaded sled.

The take-off over the frozen lake had been smooth. Then had come the strange feeling in Alec's stomach when Nick banked the plane and headed for Port Radium!

How small the Post looked! Just a tiny wooden terminal on the great frozen whiteness.

Sometimes Nick shouted at them above the roar of the engine, pointing out things down below— the hills farther up the coast—the spot of blue Arctic Ocean far out over the ice. Somewhere out there, sick people were depending on Mr. Evans to bring a doctor. And now Mr. Evans was depending on Nick to bring the doctor.

432

Soon the Post and the seacoast were far behind as they flew inland. They didn't talk much. It was hard to shout over the noise of the plane. They flew on for a long time over this empty white land. There were no trees, no settlements. just the uneven ground covered with snow. Alec wondered how a pilot could ever find his way.

Suddenly Nick turned and smiled and pointed down. "Caribou!" he said. He banked the plane so the boys could easily see below.

"Caribou!" Nanook whispered.

Caribou! There must be thousands of them! Thousands and thousands! A brown sea of animals in motion over the frozen plain. They would stop only to scratch up moss hidden beneath the snow and feed on it.

433

What hunting there would be when these great herds of caribou moved up toward the coast! Then the seal hunting would be over, and all the Eskimos around Stringer Inlet would come inland to hunt caribou. They depended on these animals for next year's food and clothing.

Alec would never have noticed Port Radium if Nick hadn't pointed it out. It was just a few buildings on the edge of Great Bear Lake, half hidden among the trees.

They landed smoothly and taxied up beside four other planes and a helicopter at the edge of the lake. Nick climbed out and then helped the boys down from the plane to stretch their legs. A man came up and told Nick that the doctor was getting ready and would be right down.

"See those buildings over there?" asked Nick. "That's the mine. We get silver there, and radium. This whole north country is being changed. It isn't the lonely Far North any more. There are mines and weather stations here. Airlines have set up regular routes in the Far North and make regular flights over these routes. A person can now buy a plane ticket for a flight by way of an air route close to the North Pole."

Just then the doctor arrived, and they flew back to the Post. He stayed a week at Stringer Inlet. With Mr. Evans he traveled out to the sealing camp. When he left, everyone had recovered or was nearly well again.

The next week Kootawuk began to build two kayaks, or Eskimo canoes, one for his son Nanook and the other for Alec Sutherland. Kootawuk would teach the boys to paddle the kayaks as soon as the ice went out.

As Alec watched Kootawuk at work, he thought proudly of his father's words: "A boy is really getting to be a man when he learns to handle a kayak."

*Clare Bice*

# When Totaram
# Washed the Elephant

Totaram was lying on his back under a tree, watching the crows play King of the Castle. They played on the long flagpole which stood in the village. One of them would fly up to the top of it. Then the others would tease him with loud voices and fly down upon him from above, trying to knock him off.

The pole was as slippery as a smooth seed, and no crow could stay king for long. But what fun he had during that time! He would flap his wings and tell them all what a fine crow he was, and then—! Down came another crow on top of him and sent him flapping into the air.

436

As Totaram lay watching this game, suddenly he heard the sound of a footstep behind him and jumped as a sleeping dog does before a cart wheel touches it.

"Have you nothing better to do than watch the crows and sleep like a bat in the daytime?" asked the man beside him.

Totaram made a deep bow, bending low from the waist, because the man was the keeper of the elephants and an important person.

"What is your mother doing?" asked the man.

"She is working in the fields," said Totaram.

"And your father?"

"He has gone to the jungle to cut bushes to put around his fields to keep out the wild pigs."

"And your sister Jai?"

"She is making something for our supper," said Totaram, who was beginning to feel very uncomfortable.

"And you?"

"I am doing nothing at all," said Totaram slowly. "But truly I would do something if I could find it to do."

"Why are you not with the other boys watching the cows?"

Totaram hung his head like wheat when the grains are ripe and heavy upon it.

"Because, O Great One," he said, "I teased one of the cows with my pointed stick. And she ran into the village and upset four bowls of milk as she ran. How could I know that she would mind the stick so much? And the milkman beat me and sent me away."

"Little Trouble Maker," said the man, "I will give you another chance. But there must be no more foolishness or teasing. You must not act like one of the monkeys in the jungle."

Totaram lifted his head.

"I want a boy to wash the big elephant," the keeper went on. "Every Wednesday and every Saturday I will take her to the pool near the gate of the city. You must meet me there when the sun is in the middle of the sky. Take with you some coconut shells to scrub with."

Totaram could hardly believe his good luck and ran off to tell the boys about it. The keeper of the elephants looked at the crow on top of the pole, and then he looked at the boys who were waving their arms about and talking.

"They are much alike, boys and crows," the keeper said smiling, and went away.

Totaram thought that Wednesday would never come. He teased the gray kitten, pulling its tail until it mewed and his sister Jai cried.

His mother sighed and said, "Little Trouble Maker, use your strong arms at this," and gave him the heavy stick to pound the brown rice.

At last Wednesday came, and when the sun was high, Totaram set out for the pool. He arrived before the elephant and sat down under a wild fig tree to wait.

Then came the elephant, like a black mountain. Totaram felt the size of a rabbit, and then he felt the size of a mouse. Then he thought, "If it comes much nearer, I shall be as nothing at all!"

The keeper laughed at him. "Are you a squirrel come to wash my elephant?" he asked. "You looked larger in your village. I could use twenty of you little ones."

Totaram's knees shook as the dry grass does in the swift winds of the hot season.

But Totaram held on to his coconut shells hard and followed the keeper down to the water. There the enormous elephant gave a sigh of happiness and lay down on her side. And Totaram climbed on top of her and began to scrub her with his coconut shells.

It was long work. "Surely I am cleaning a mile of elephant," he said to himself, and looked hopefully to see if the keeper would say that his work was finished. But the man was smoking a water pipe and was lost in thought.

440

Totaram had long since forgotten to be afraid, and he even dared to scrub in the elephant's big ears and around her little eyes.

That evening when he went home, he had money in his pocket, and he was so proud that he called all his friends together to tell them what a wonderful boy he was. And he pulled the gray kitten's tail again.

When Saturday came, Jai and two village boys followed Totaram into the city and to the pool. The keeper lay down and went to sleep under the wild fig tree. And Totaram began scrubbing behind the elephant's ears as though he had been cleaning elephant's ears all his life.

"O my grandfathers!" said one of the boys. "Her right ear is as large as my father's dinner plate."

"Her left ear is the size of my uncle's umbrella," said the other boy. "Aren't you afraid, Totaram?"

"Oh my, no," said Totaram. "The elephant may be enormous, with ears like umbrellas, but she is as stupid as a mountain."

He began to jump up and down on her back to show them how brave he was

441

The elephant moved one ear slowly, like a banana leaf in the wind. Totaram went on jumping. The elephant moved the other ear slowly, like a sail in a fishing boat. Totaram went on jumping.

Suddenly the elephant reached up her trunk, took Totaram around the waist and ducked him in the muddy water. Then she lifted him up and shook him the way a cat does a mouse. Then she ducked him again. Jai and the two boys laughed until they tumbled down and gasped for breath.

"She is as stupid as a mountain, is she?" called one boy.

"Now you know how my gray kitten feels when you pull its tail," said Jai.

"O queen of elephants," cried Totaram, "set me down, and I will never pull the gray kitten's tail again."

The elephant shook him again.

"O wisest of elephants," said Totaram, "truly I will never jump on you again."

Then the elephant set him down, and he ran away into the jungle near the village, where he could not see Jai and the two boys, who were still laughing.

Late that afternoon his mother found him there with his head on a gray root, fast asleep. He was saying something, and when she leaned over him, she heard, "Truly I will never pull the gray kitten's tail again."

*Irene Mott Bose*

443

# Things to Think About and Do

1. List the stories in which each of the following things appear. Be ready to tell why each thing is important to people in the story.

| | | | |
|---|---|---|---|
| caves | reindeer | skis | cache |
| kayak | lassoes | caribou | radium |

2. What special meanings do the underlined words below have in the stories?

<u>sealing</u> camp (page 424)
a brown <u>sea</u> of animals (page 433)
a <u>mile</u> of elephant (page 440)
<u>spring</u> from a rock (page 398)
<u>fresher</u> pastures (page 410)
would <u>strike</u> again (page 415)
<u>sank</u> on one knee (page 409)

Write sentences using each of these words with another meaning.

3. Abd el Karuzeh and Lars were both herders. How were their jobs, as described in the stories, different? How were their homes different? Why were they different? Make a chart showing the differences and give a reason for each difference.

4. What new skill would Alec and Nanook learn during the long summer days ahead? List a skill that you are likely to learn this summer.

5. The magazine for which you are taking pictures is now sending you to the Far North. Decide what kind of a story you will write about the Far North. List a name for it and five pictures that you will take to go with the story.

6. Work with a committee on an outline map of the world for the bulletin board. Try to show where most of the stories or poems in this reader may have taken place.

7. How is a trip under the North Pole different from a flight over it? How do men travel under polar ice? What adventures might you have under the polar ice?

8. There are many different words that describe how a person is speaking in a story. Choose one of the following words to tell how each person in the sentences below spoke.

| | | |
|---|---|---|
| ordered | gasped | grunted |
| exclaimed | whispered | yelled |

"Shoo!" he __?__ above the roar of the falls.
"Caribou," Nanook __?__ softly to himself.
"Return to the herd at once," __?__ Father Turi.
"Wolves! Wolves!" the woman __?__ breathlessly.
"Uh-huh," he __?__, "I told you so."
"What an enormous elephant!" __?__ Totaram.

# Some Books to Read

*All Alone*, by Claire Huchet Bishop.

Two boys tend their herds in the Swiss mountains and learn the meaning of friendship in the face of danger.

*The Family under the Bridge*, by Natalie Savage Carlson.

This is an unusual story about a family of children who lived in Paris and the kind-hearted old hobo who came to their rescue.

*Kaatje and the Christmas Compass*, by Alta H. Seymour.

A brother and sister have some holiday adventures in Holland.

*Nils, the Island Boy*, by Hedvig Collin.

Nine-year-old Nils lives in Denmark where the famous storyteller Hans Christian Andersen was born.

*Panchito*, by Loren D. Good.

A Mexican parrot becomes bored with life and sets out to find a livelier home. Exciting and amusing adventures follow.

*The Spettecake Holiday*, by Edith Unnerstad.

After a summer filled with adventures, the boy in this story about Sweden keeps his promise about the wonderful spettecake.

446

# Your Glossary

The glossary will help you to pronounce and understand the meanings of hard words in this book. A number after a definition indicates the first page on which the word has been used with that particular meaning.

The list below shows you how each marked vowel is pronounced. It is called a pronunciation key.

ā lāte    ē wē    ō ōld    o͞o mo͞on
ă ăm    ĕ wĕt    ŏ nŏt    o͝o fo͝ot
ä färm    ē̃ lettē̃r    ô hôrse    oi oil
ȧ ȧsk    ī hīde    ǒ sǒft    ou out
â câre    ǐ hǐd    ū ūse
                                       ŭ ŭs
                                       û bûrn

## A

**a ban'don** (ȧ băn'dŭn). To leave behind; to give up. (402)

**Abd el Ka ru'zeh** (äbd ĕl kă ro͞o'zĕ). The name of a shepherd boy in the hill country of North Africa. (397)

**ache** (āk). 1. To have pain. (175) 2. A pain that continues.

**a'cre** (ā'kē̃r). A piece of land equal to 4,840 square yards. (187)

**ac'tion** (ăk'shŭn). 1. The doing of something. (283) 2. A deed; an act.

**a dapt'** (ȧ dăpt'). 1. To adjust; as, to a new way of life. (269) 2. To make fit or suitable.

**a diós'** (ä dyōs'). Spanish word for *good-by*. (56)

**Af'ri ca** (ăf'rĭ kȧ). A continent of the Eastern Hemisphere, south of Europe. (259)

**Al'ba ny** (ôl'bȧ nĭ). The capital of the State of New York. (140)

**al'der** (ôl'dē̃r). A tree or shrub of the birch family. (238)

**a lert'** (ȧ lûrt'). 1. Watchful, especially against danger. (232) 2. Brisk; nimble; active.

**an'chor** (ăng'kē̃r). 1. To make fast by means of a heavy weight. (359) 2. A heavy piece of iron or steel with hooks at one end and a crossbar at the other. An anchor is used to hold a ship in place.

**ant'eat er** (ănt'ēt ē̃r). An animal whose food is ants which it licks up with its long tongue. (277)

Anteater.

**anx'ious** (ăngk'shŭs). 1. Eager; desiring very much. (187) 2. Worried or fearful.

**A pol'lo** (ȧ pŏl'ō). A Greek god of manly youth and beauty, and of poetry, music, and prophecy. He was called the sun god. (99)

447

**arch** (ärch). 1. To bend like an arch. (249) 2. An opening with a curved top, such as a doorway. 3. Anything that is shaped like

Arch.

an arch; as, the *arch* of the foot.

**Arc'tic** (ärk'tĭk). 1. The region around the North Pole. (272) 2. Of or having to do with the North Pole or the region near it; as, the *arctic* fox.

**Ar i zo'na** (ăr ĭ zō'nà). A state in the southwestern part of the United States. (339)

**A'sia** (ā'zhà). A continent of the Eastern Hemisphere. It is the largest continent on the globe. (274)

**a tom'ic** (à tŏm'ĭk). 1. Of or having to do with atoms; as, *atomic* power. (158) 2. Very, very small.

**at ten'tion** (à tĕn'shŭn). 1. The act or power of fixing one's mind closely upon something. (117) 2. A position of readiness; as, to stand at *attention*. 3. A thoughtful act of kindness or courtesy.

**awk'ward** (ôk'wĕrd). 1. Not easy or graceful in movement; clumsy. (210) 2. Not well suited to use; not convenient; as, an *awkward* tool.

## B

**ba boon'** (bă bōōn'). A large ape with a doglike face. Baboons are found in Africa and Asia. (260)

**bal'ance** (băl'ăns). 1. To keep oneself steady in order not to fall; also, to keep an object steady. (364) 2. Steadiness; firmness. 3. An instrument for weighing things.

**bar'ri er** (băr'ĭ ĕr). 1. A gate or bar that marks the start of a race. (337) 2. A fence, railing, or gate that keeps out anything.

Barrier.

**beam** (bēm). 1. A ray of light or heat. (87) 2. A long, heavy piece of timber or metal, used to support a building or ship.

**beech** (bēch). A tree with smooth gray bark and dark-green leaves. It bears small, sweet nuts. (202)

**Be'ring Sea** (bēr'ĭng sē). The northern part of the Pacific Ocean. It lies between Alaska and northeast Asia. (231)

**blend** (blĕnd). 1. To mix one thing with another. (272) 2. A mixture of things; as, a *blend* of tea or of colors.

**Bob'ry** (bŏb'rĭ). The name of a baby otter that lived in the Bering Sea. (231)

**bold** (bōld). 1. Brave; daring. (143) 2. Too forward; rude.

**Boones'bor ough** (bōōnz'bûr ō). A fort in Kentucky named in honor of Daniel Boone. (61)

**Bos'ton** (bŏs'tŭn). The capital of the State of Massachusetts. (206)

**Brah'man** (brä'măn). A Hindu of the highest caste in India. (102)

# C

**cache** (kăsh). 1. A place for hiding or storing food or other supplies. (424) 2. Food or supplies thus hidden or stored.

**Can′a da** (kăn′á dá). A country on the continent of North America. (248)

**Ca na′di an** (ká nā′dĭ ăn). 1. Having to do with Canada or its people. (253) 2. A native or inhabitant of Canada.

**cap′tive** (kăp′tĭv). 1. Made or held prisoner. (248) 2. A prisoner, especially a prisoner of war.

**car′i bou** (kăr′ĭ bōō). A reindeer of Greenland and the northern part of North America. (427)

**car′riage** (kăr′ĭj). 1. A wheeled vehicle for carrying persons. (86) 2. Manner of holding the head and body; bearing.

**cha′os** (kā′ŏs). A condition of great confusion or complete disorder. (154)

**chest′nut** (chĕs′nŭt). 1. An eatable nut that grows on certain trees of the beech family. (364) 2. The tree on which such a nut grows.

**Chi ca′go** (shĭ kô′gō). A large city in northeastern Illinois. It is on Lake Michigan. (144)

**chis′el** (chĭz′'l). 1. A tool with a sharp edge at one end, used to chip away wood, stone, etc. (86) 2. To chip or cut with a chisel.

Chisel.

**Clin′ton, De Witt′** (klĭn′tŭn, dē wĭt′). 1. The name given to an early American locomotive. (132) 2. A famous governor of New York State.

**clutch** (klŭch). 1. A grasp or grip; as, with fingers or claws. (240) 2. To grip with the hands or with the claws. 3. To snatch.

**co lo′nes** (kŏ lō′nās). Money used in Costa Rica. (181)

**col′o ny** (kŏl′ō nĭ). 1. A group of animals of the same kind living close together. (348) 2. A group of persons who have moved from their native land and settled in a new land.

**con di′tion** (kŏn dĭsh′ŭn). 1. State of health; fitness. (222) 2. Something necessary to the happening of something else.

**Cos′ta Ri′ca** (kŏs′tá rē′ká). A republic in Central America. (172)

**crag** (krăg). 1. A rock that stands out in a point on high ground. (397) 2. A rough, broken cliff.

**crick** (krĭk). A painful condition of the muscles in which one or more of them seem to tighten or draw together. (297)

**crick′et** (krĭk′ĕt). 1. A small, jumping insect noted for the chirping notes made by the males. (93) 2. An outdoor game played with bats, ball, and wickets, usually with eleven players on each side.

Cricket.

---

lāte, ăm, färm, ȧsk, câre, wē, wĕt, lettẽr, hīde, hĭd, ōld, nŏt, hôrse, sŏft, ūse, ŭs, bûrn, mōōn, fŏŏt, oil, out

**crouch** (krouch). 1. To stoop or bend low to the ground; as, a person hiding or an animal waiting to jump on its prey. (78) 2. The act of stooping or bending low.

**crys'tal** (krĭs'tăl). 1. Clear; transparent. (154) 2. A clear, transparent mineral. 3. Glass that is very clear and brilliant. 4. Glass over the face of a watch.

**cu ri os'i ty** (kū rĭ ŏs'ĭ tĭ). 1. An eager wish to learn; the state of being curious. (244) 2. A strange or unusual thing.

**cush'ion** (kŏŏsh'ŭn). 1. A soft pillow to rest on or against. (285) 2. To put on a cushion.

**cy'clone** (sī'klōn). A storm with strong winds blowing inward or around a calm center. As a figure of speech, a thing or things moving swiftly around something else like a strong, whirling wind. (266)

**cyg'net** (sĭg'nĕt). A young swan. (252)

### D

**Daed'a lus** (dĕd'á lŭs). The builder of a labyrinth, a place filled with winding and confusing passageways. A Greek myth about him is told in the story "The Flight of Icarus." (95)

**dam'age** (dăm'ĭj). 1. Injury; harm. (124) 2. To harm; to injure.

**de bate'** (dē bāt'). 1. A discussion for and against a question. (382) 2. To take part in the discussion of a question.

**des'ert** (dĕz'ẽrt). 1. Dry and barren with little rainfall. (268) 2. A dry, barren region where few plants grow.

**de sign'** (dē zīn'). 1. The way details are arranged in a piece of work; the pattern. (178) 2. To make a pattern or sketch of something.

Design.

**de stroy'** (dē stroi'). To kill; to put an end to. (81)

**dig'ni ty** (dĭg'nĭ tĭ). Stately manner; self-respect; also, the importance, rank, or honor of a person. (290)

**dis cour'age** (dĭs kûr'ĭj). To take away or make less one's courage; to cause one to lose heart. (84)

**dit'ty** (dĭt'ĭ). A short, simple poem or song. (258)

### E

**ech'o** (ĕk'ō). 1. The repeating of a sound or sounds already heard. An echo is caused by the throwing back of sound waves; as, from a cliff or hill. (31) 2. To send back or repeat a sound.

**Eng'land** (ĭng'glănd). A part of Great Britain, south of Scotland. (133)

**e nor'mous** (ē nôr'mŭs). Very, very large; huge. (440)

**en vi'ron ment** (ĕn vī'rŭn mĕnt). Surroundings; the conditions and influences that surround and affect the growth and development of a person, an animal, or a plant. (269)

**es cape'** (ĕs kāp'). 1. To get free; to get out and away; as, by flight. (95) 2. To avoid; as, to *escape* punishment. 3. The act of getting free. 4. The means; as, a fire *escape*.

**Es'ki mo** (ĕs'kĭ mō). A member of a race that lives on the arctic coasts of America. (234)

**etch** (ĕch). To draw clear, sharp lines as if cut by acid on metal. (211)

**ex act'** (ĕg zăkt'). Precise; definite; also, correct. (152)

**ex cite'ment** (ĕk sīt'mĕnt). 1. The condition of being excited, or having the feelings stirred up. (80) 2. Anything that excites or stirs up.

**ex cur'sion** (ĕks kûr'zhŭn). A trip made chiefly for fun and a good time. (137)

**ex per'i ment** (ĕks pĕr'ĭ mĕnt). 1. A test or trial to find out about something that is doubtful or unknown. (155) 2. To test something.

**F**

**fa'mous** (fā'mŭs). Very well known; much talked about. (65)

**Fe ra'gi** (fĕ rä'zhĕ). The younger son of a Headman in the hill country of North Africa. (401)

**fer'ry** (fĕr'ĭ). 1. A boat that carries persons or things across a river or narrow body of water. 2. A special

Ferry.

air service used to ferry persons and things over a regular route between two points. (157) 3. A place where something is carried by boat across a river or other body of water.

**fierce** (fērs). Savage; wild; violent (62)

**floe** (flō). A field or sheet of floating ice. (396)

**fore'head** (fŏr'ĕd). The part of the face above the eyes; the brow. (38)

**Fram Point** (frăm point). A small point of land on the northern coast of Canada. (427)

**Fuad** (fwăd). The elder son of a Headman in the hill country of North Africa. (401)

**G**

**glis'ten** (glĭs''n). To sparkle or shine. (423)

**gloom** (glōōm). 1. Darkness; deep shadow; dim light. (211) 2. Sadness.

**glo'ri ous** (glō'rĭ ŭs). 1. Splendid; very delightful. (97) 2. Noble; worthy of praise; as, a *glorious* deed.

**gorge** (gôrj). 1. A narrow passage; as, one between two mountains; a ravine with steep, rocky sides. (371) 2. To eat greedily until one is full.

Gorge.

---

lāte, ăm, färm, ȧsk, câre, wē, wĕt, lettẽr, hīde, hĭd, ōld, nŏt, hôrse, sŏft, ūse, ŭs, bûrn, mōōn, fŏŏt, oil, out

**graze** (grāz). 1. To feed on grass and other growing things. (119) 2. To rub or touch lightly in passing.

**grief** (grēf). Suffering of the mind, as a result of sorrow or trouble; great sadness. (101)

**grouch'y** (grouch'ĭ). Sullen; sulky; showing crossness. (200)

**grum'ble** (grŭm'b'l). 1. To rumble; as, a cart on a rough road. (34) 2. To mutter with discontent; to find fault. (74)

### H

**har'vest** (här'vĕst). 1. The gathering of a crop. (186) 2. A crop, such as vegetables or fruit. 3. To reap or gather.

**home'ly** (hōm'lĭ). Plain in appearance; not handsome or beautiful. (134)

**hon'or** (ŏn'ẽr). 1. (written with a capital letter) A title given to show respect; as, *His Honor*, the Mayor. (323) 2. Respect.

**huge** (hūj). Very large; enormous. (78)

**hull** (hŭl).
1. The frame or body of a ship. (160)
2. The outer covering of a

Hull of Ship.

fruit or seed. 3. To remove the hulls from something; as, to *hull* berries.

**hu'man** (hū'măn). 1. A man, woman, or child; a human being. (98) 2. Belonging or relating to man.

**hy'dro gen** (hī'drō jĕn). A colorless gas which has no odor or taste. It is the lightest substance known. (158)

**hy e'na** (hī ē'nȧ). A large, strong animal that hunts by night. Hyenas are found in Asia and Africa. (399)

### I

**Ic'a rus** (ĭk'ȧ rŭs). The son of Daedalus, who, with his father, escaped from the island of Crete by means of wings made from feathers. (95)

**In'di a** (ĭn'dĭ ȧ). A country of southern Asia. (102)

**in'land** (ĭn'lănd). 1. Toward the interior of a country; away from the coast. (427) 2. The part of a country in from the coast or boundaries.

**in'let** (ĭn'lĕt). A narrow strip of water running into the land or between islands; a bay or cove in a shore line. (250)

### J

**jack'al** (jăk'ôl). A wild dog of Asia and Africa. (102)

**Jai** (jī). The name of a girl who lived in India. (437)

**Je mi'ma** (jē mĭ'mȧ). The name of Daniel Boone's daughter. (62)

**jig'sawed** (jĭg'sôd). 1. Cut in curved lines like a jigsaw puzzle. 2. As a figure of speech, puzzled. (317)

**Jinx** (jĭngks). 1. The name of a cat in "Freddy, the Detective." (282) 2. Something that brings bad luck; a *jinx* is a hoodoo.

452

**John Bull** (jŏn bōŏl). 1. The name of an early English locomotive. (133) 2. A nickname for England and Englishmen.

**judg'ment** (jŭj'mĕnt). 1. A decision given after judging. (103) 2. The decision or sentence of a court. 3. The power of deciding wisely.

### K

**kay'ak** (kī'ăk). An Eskimo canoe, which is usually made of sealskin. (435)

Kayak.

**Ken tuck'y** (kĕn tŭk'ĭ). A state in the east central part of the United States. It is just south of the Ohio River. (60)

**king'dom** (kĭng'dŭm). A country ruled by a king. (81)

**Kit'ty Hawk** (kĭt'ĭ hôk). A village on a sandy barrier in the eastern part of North Carolina, where the Wright brothers made the first airplane flight in the United States. (122)

**Koot'a wuk** (kōō'tå wŭk). The name of an Eskimo man. (431)

### L

**lan'tern** (lăn'tẽrn). A case for protecting a light from something; as, wind or rain. (12)

Lantern.

**Lapp** (lăp). A member of a race living in Lapland, a region in the far north of Europe, above the Arctic Circle. (410)

**Lars** (lärz). The name of a boy whose home was in Lapland. (410)

**lash** (lăsh). 1. Short for *eyelash*. (275) 2. A blow with a whip. 3. Anything used for whipping. 4. To strike a person with a lash.

**las'so** (lăs'ō). 1. A rope or long leather thong, with a noose at one end. (411) 2. To catch an animal with a *lasso*.

**ledge** (lĕj). 1. A shelf or ridge of rock. (400) 2. A reef, usually one under water near shore.

**lev'el** (lĕv'ĕl). Having a flat, even surface. (123)

**Lin'coln** (lĭng'kŭn). The sixteenth President of the United States. (210)

**lit'ter** (lĭt'ẽr). 1. The young animals born all at one time to a dog or other animal. (214) 2. Things lying around in disorder. 3. Straw or hay used as bedding for animals.

**Lo'co mo bile** (lō'kō mō bēl). One of the early automobiles that was run by steam instead of gasoline. (118)

**lurk** (lûrk). To wait out of sight; to move secretly. (423)

**lye** (lī). A strong liquid made by putting water through wood ashes. (189)

### M

**mar'ten** (mär'tĕn). A thin-bodied animal that has a long tail and fine gray or brown fur. (239)

---

lāte, ăm, färm, åsk, câre, wē, wĕt, lettẽr, hīde, hĭd, ōld, nŏt, hôrse, sŏft, ūse, ŭs, bûrn, mōōn, fŏŏt, oil, out

**Me len'dy** (mĕ lĕn'dĭ). The name of the four motherless children in the story "The Back of the Bus." (33)

**Mer'chan dise Mart** (mûr'chăn dīz märt). 1. A very large building in Chicago where household furnishings are on display. (144) 2. A store or market place where many things are sold.

**mer'maid** (mûr'mād). A mythical sea creature with the upper part of its body like the body of a woman and the lower part like that of a fish. (423)

Mermaid.

**mi'grate** (mī'grāt). 1. To move regularly from one place to another; as, for food. (372) 2. To move from one country or region to another.

**min'er al** (mĭn'ẽr ăl). Something in nature that is neither animal nor plant; as, gold, silver, iron, coal. Many rocks are solid minerals. (349)

**mon stros'i ty** (mŏn strŏs'ĭ tĭ). Something very large and unusual in appearance; a monster. (117)

**mon'u ment** (mŏn'ū mĕnt). Something by which we remember a person or a happening, such as a statue, building, or arch. (347)

**mo'tion less** (mō'shŭn lĕs). Without motion; not able to move. (92)

**mound** (mound). 1. A heap; a rounded pile of something. (241) 2. A hill or knoll. 3. The place where the pitcher stands in a baseball game. (296)

**Mur rie'ta, Joa quin'** (mo͞or ryā'tä, wä kēn'). A bandit of olden days in California. (48)

**mu se'um** (mū zē'ŭm). A building in which are kept and shown things of interest and works of art. (32)

**mys te'ri ous** (mĭs tēr'ĭ ŭs). Full of mystery; hard to explain. (8)

**N**

**Na'nook** (nă'no͝ok). The name of an Eskimo boy. (424)

**neigh** (nā). 1. The cry of a horse. (134) 2. To give the cry of a horse.

**New York** (nū yôrk'). 1. A Middle Atlantic state in the eastern part of the United States. 2. A seaport city at the mouth of the Hudson River in New York State. (294)

**Ni ag'a ra Falls'** (nī ăg'ȧ rȧ fôlz'). Great falls of the Niagara River flowing from Lake Erie to Lake Ontario. (368)

**nick'el** (nĭk'ĕl). 1. A five-cent piece. (373) 2. A hard silver-white metal.

**non'sense** (nŏn'sĕns). Meaningless actions or words; foolishness. (116)

**nought** (nôt). 1. Nothing; not a bit. (93) 2. A zero.

**nui'sance** (nū'săns). A person or thing that is annoying or troublesome. (115)

**O**

**o be'di ence** (ō bē'dĭ ĕns). The act of obeying. (222)

**Ol'i phant** (ŏl'ĭ fănt). A character in "The Back of the Bus." (33)

o pin'ion (ō pĭn'yŭn). What one thinks; belief; also, judgment about a person or thing. (103)

or'bit (ôr'bĭt). The path taken by a heavenly body revolving around another body; as, the earth's *orbit* around the sun. (160)

out'raged (out'rājd). Offended; insulted; treated in a shameful way. (290)

## P

part'ner (pärt'nẽr). 1. One of two or more persons who run a business together. (184) 2. A person who shares something with another person or persons. 3. In games, one who plays on the same side or on the same team.

pa'tient (pā'shĕnt). 1. Showing steady effort in doing something. (91) 2. Bearing pain or trouble without complaining. 3. A person under a doctor's care. (114)

pa trol' (pȧ trōl'). 1. A going of the rounds to watch or guard a place. (427) 2. To go the rounds of a place as a policeman or watchman.

peer (pēr). To look closely as if to see better. (244)

pen'guin (pĕn'gwĭn). A sea bird found chiefly in the cold regions of the Southern Hemisphere. It can swim but not fly. (277)

Penguin.

pil'lar (pĭl'ẽr). A firm upright support, such as a column; therefore, something that gives a firm support. The man was a *pillar* of strength. (391)

plan ta'tion (plăn tā'shŭn). A place planted to a special crop, such as sugar cane or cotton, and using many field workers. (172)

plas'tic (plăs'tĭk). 1. Easily molded or shaped. 2. A nonmetallic substance that can be easily molded or shaped, but is solid in the finished state. (157)

plen'ty (plĕn'tĭ). More than enough; abundant; as, *plenty* of time to get somewhere. (276)

poise (poiz). 1. To balance; to hold or make firm or steady. (154) 2. Balance; steadiness.

po'lar (pō'lẽr). Having to do with the North Pole or South Pole; also, lying near or coming from either pole. (268)

pomp'ous (pŏmp'ŭs). Acting with dignity or proudly; trying to seem important. (290)

por'ridge (pŏr'ĭj). Food made by boiling a cereal or vegetable in water or milk until it thickens. (411)

Port Ra'di um (pōrt rā'dĭ ŭm). The name of a town on the shore of Great Bear Lake in northern Canada. (431)

pos ses'sion (pŏ zĕsh'ŭn). Something which is held as one's own; something owned. (177)

---

lāte, ăm, färm, ȧsk, câre, wē, wĕt, lettẽr, hīde, hĭd, ōld, nŏt, hôrse, sŏft, ūse, ŭs, bûrn, mōon, fŏŏt, oil, out

**prompt** (prŏmpt). Quick and ready to act; also, done at once. (305)

**prow** (prou). The forward part of a ship; the bow. (423)

## Q

Quiver.

**quiv'er** (kwĭv'ẽr). 1. To shake or shiver, usually from excitement. (258) 2. A case for carrying arrows.

## R

**ra'di um** (rā'dĭ ŭm). A radioactive element found in small amounts in certain minerals. (434)

**Re bec'ca** (rē bĕk'à). The name of Daniel Boone's wife. (58)

**reg'u lar** (rĕg'ū lẽr). 1. Steady in course or practice; usual. (434) 2. Even in form, make-up, or kind; as, *regular* features.

**reins** (rānz). The straps of a bridle, fastened to the bit, used to control a horse or other animal. (16)

**re lief'** (rē lēf'). The removal of a burden, pain, difficulty, or danger. (401)

**res'cue** (rĕs'kū). To save from danger or harm; to set free. (29)

**res er va'tion** (rĕz ẽr vā'shŭn). 1. Land set aside by the government for a special use; as, for the Indians, for a school, or for a park. (369) 2. Something that is reserved; as, a room in a hotel.

**re spon si bil'i ty** (rē spŏn sǐ bǐl'ǐ tǐ). Something for which a person is responsible; a task or duty needing much attention. (380)

**ridge** (rǐj).

Mountain Ridge.

1. A row of hills or mountains. (369) 2. A raised line or strip of something; as, the *ridge* of a roof.

**Ro ber'to** (rŏ bẽr'tō). The name of the brother of Tony, a boy who lived in Costa Rica. (172)

**ro'tor** (rō'tẽr). 1. One of the parts in a machine that turns, or revolves, in a part that does not move. 2. A system of revolving blades that gives all or most of the lift supporting a helicopter. (146)

**rough** (rŭf). 1. Not gentle. (82) 2. Not smooth. 3. Unfinished; as, a *rough* drawing.

**route** (rōot). The road or the way which is, or is to be, traveled; as, on a trip. (434)

**roy'al** (roi'ăl). 1. Having to do with the government of a kingdom. (255) 2. Suitable for a king.

**rush'es** (rŭsh'ĕz). Hollow-stemmed plants that grow in swampy land. (251)

Rushes.

**rus'tle** (rŭs''l). 1. To move so as to make small sounds, like leaves blowing in the wind. (230) 2. A sound like the moving of dry leaves.

## S

**San Joa quin'** (săn wä kēn'). A river and valley in California. (47)

456

**sav'age** (săv'ĭj). 1. Wild; untamed; also, fierce; cruel. (406) 2. Not civilized.

**scarce'ly** (skârs'lĭ). Hardly ever; not quite; almost not. (272)

**scent** (sĕnt). 1. An odor; a smell. (238) 2. To fill with an odor.

**Sche nec'ta dy** (skĕ nĕk'tȧ dĭ). A city in the State of New York. (138)

**scorn** (skôrn). 1. A feeling of anger or disgust. 2. To look upon as not worthy of notice. (76)

**Scot'land** (skŏt'lănd). The northern part of Great Britain. (90)

**scowl** (skoul). 1. To look cross or angry by wrinkling up the brows. (206) 2. An angry or cross look; a frown.

**sea'son** (sē'z'n). 1. To dry or harden; to age; as, to *season* lumber. (210) 2. To make food more pleasant to the taste by adding salt, pepper, or some spice. 3. One of the four parts of the year; as, spring, summer, autumn, winter. (348)

**seize** (sēz). To take hold of a person or thing suddenly. (79)

**Se ño ri'ta** (sā nyō rē'tä). 1. Spanish word for *young lady*. (56) 2. A title meaning *Miss*.

**ser'geant** (sär'jĕnt). 1. A police officer next below a captain in rank. (255) 2. An army officer ranking next above a corporal.

**set'tle ment** (sĕt''l mĕnt). 1. A small village; a colony. (59) 2. Payment; as, of a bill.

**shag'gy** (shăg'ĭ). Thick and rough. (201)

**shal'low** (shăl'ō). Not deep. (242)

**shift** (shĭft). To change from one direction to another; also, to change something from one place to another. (288)

**Sic'i ly** (sĭs'ĭ lĭ). An Italian island southwest of Italy. (99)

**slope** (slōp). 1. To slant. (37) 2. A slanting position or direction.

**soar** (sōr). To fly upward on wings, or as if on wings. (77)

**so'fa** (sō'fa). A long seat or couch, usually upholstered, and with back and arms. (41)

**Span'ish** (spăn'ĭsh). 1. The language of Spain. (180) 2. Of or having to do with Spain.

**spire** (spīr). A pointed roof of a tower; a steeple. (154)

**sprawl** (sprôl). 1. To spread out in an irregular way. (154) 2. To lie or sit with the arms or legs spread out in an awkward way.

**squawk** (skwôk). 1. To make a loud, harsh scream. (305) 2. A loud, harsh scream.

**stern** (stûrn). 1. The rear end of a boat. (204) 2. Severe; strict; grim. (382)

**stom'ach** (stŭm'ăk). The organ of digestion into which food goes after it has left the mouth and passed down the throat. (195)

**stride** (strīd). 1. A long, regular step. . (273) 2. To walk or run with long, regular steps.

---

lāte, ăm, färm, ȧsk, câre, wē, wĕt, lettēr, hīde, hĭd, ōld, nŏt, hôrse, sŏft, ūse, ŭs, bûrn, mōōn, fŏŏt, oil, out

457

**strife** (strīf). A struggle; a fight. (367)

**String'er In'let** (strĭng'ẽr ĭn'lĕt). An inlet on the northern coast of Canada. (426)

**struc'ture** (strŭk'tũr). 1. The way something is put together or built, such as the body of a person or animal, or of a building. (273) 2. Something built; as, a bridge.

**sum'mons** (sŭm'ŭnz). A call to attend to some duty. (367)

**Sur'-Dah** (sûr'dȧ). The name of a young lion whose home was in Africa. (259)

**swan** (swŏn). A large water bird, usually white, with a very long neck. (248)

**swarm** (swôrm). 1. A large crowd; a great number. (266) 2. A colony of bees.

**swoop** (swo͞op). To come down with a rush, or to pounce on suddenly, like a hawk attacking its prey. (232)

## T

**tan'trum** (tăn'trŭm). A fit of bad temper. (154)

**tem'ple** (tĕm'p'l). 1. A building for worship. (101) 2. The space between the eyes and forehead and the upper part of the ears.

**ter'ri er** (tĕr'ĭ ẽr). A kind of dog once used in hunting but now usually kept as a pet. A terrier is small, smart, brave, and lively. (212)

**throb** (thrŏb). To vibrate; to beat fast or hard. (13)

**throt'tle** (thrŏt''l). To stop or check the flow of something, such as steam or gasoline, by closing a valve or lever. (147)

**tilt** (tĭlt). To tip; to cause to slope. (146)

**Tim buc'too** (tĭm bŭk'to͞o). A place in French West Africa. (329)

**Tom'os** (tŏm'ŏs). The name of a herder of reindeer in Lapland. (411)

**ton** (tŭn). A measure of weight, usually 2,000 pounds. (270)

**To'ta ram** (tō'tä räm). A boy who was nicknamed "Little Trouble Maker." (436)

**tour'ist** (to͞or'ĭst). A person who travels for the fun of it. (166)

**tri'al** (trī'ăl). 1. A test of some kind. (222) 2. The hearing and judging of a case in a law court.

**trop'i cal** (trŏp'ĭ kăl). Having to do with or happening in the tropics, the region near the equator. (268)

**trum'pet** (trŭm'pĕt). A musical wind instrument that has a very strong tone. (248)

Trumpet.

**Tu'ri** (tū'rĭ). The name of a family who lived in Lapland. (410)

**tusk** (tŭsk). In certain animals, a very large, long tooth, used to dig up food and to fight off enemies. Tusks usually grow in pairs. (270)

## U

**un a ware'** (ŭn ȧ wâr'). Not aware; not conscious of; ignorant; as, *unaware* of danger. (328)

**u'ni corn** (ū'nĭ kôrn). An imaginary animal like a horse but having a long horn in the middle of its forehead. (83)

**u ra'ni um** (ū rā'nĭ ŭm). A heavy, hard, nickel-white metal that is radioactive. (163)

**U'tah** (ū'tô). A state in the western part of the United States. (348)

## V

**vag'a bond** (văg'à bŏnd). A person who wanders from place to place; a tramp. (396)

**veld** (vĕlt). A grassland in South Africa. It may have scattered bushes and a few trees. (259)

## W

**war'y** (wâr'ĭ). Cautious; careful; on one's guard against danger. (422)

**Wash'ing ton** (wŏsh'ĭng tŭn). 1. The first President of the United States. (367) 2. The capital of the United States. 3. A state in the northwestern part of the United States.

**wea'ry** (wēr'ĭ). Worn out; very tired. (210)

**web** (wĕb). 1. The fine network spread by a spider to catch small insects; a cobweb. (90) 2. The skin between the toes of many water birds and some animals.

**Wheel'wright** (hwēl'rīt). 1. The name of a traffic officer in the story about the Melendy family. (39) 2. A man who makes and repairs wheels.

**whim'per** (hwĭm'pẽr). 1. A low, broken cry. (265) 2. To make a low crying sound as if in trouble.

**whip poor will'** (hwĭp pōor wĭl'). A night-flying bird of eastern North America. It is named from its peculiar call. (367)

Whippoorwill.

**whith'er** (hwĭth'ẽr). To what place? (422)

**wil'de beest** (wĭl'dĕ bēst). A large antelope found in Africa; a gnu. (259)

Wildebeest.

**wil'der ness** (wĭl'dẽr nĕs). A wild region where no people live; a waste. (60)

**wiz'ard** (wĭz'ẽrd). 1. A person who is supposed to have magic power; a magician. (86) 2. In common use, a very capable person.

**wound** (wōond). 1. A hurt or injury to the body. (40) 2. A hurt to one's feelings. 3. To hurt or injure.

**Wright, Or'ville** and **Wil'bur** (rīt, ôr'vĭl *and* wĭl'bẽr). American pioneers in aviation. (122)

## Y

**yah hya ris** (yä hī rĭs). Words of a shepherd's song in North Africa. (403)

---

lāte, ăm, färm, ȧsk, câre, wē, wĕt, lettẽr, hīde, hĭd, ōld, nŏt, hôrse, sŏft, ūse, ŭs, bûrn, mōon, fŏŏt, oil, out

# To the Teacher

This Fourth Reader, *Roads to Everywhere,* follows *Friends Far and Near,* the Third Reader, Level II, of the GINN BASIC READING SERIES.

This Fourth Reader introduces 691 new words and, except for proper nouns and sound words, maintains 97 per cent of the words taught at the earlier levels of this series.

The starred words appear also in the glossary. Those in italics are foreign words or words found only in the poems. Except for a few pages of poetry, not more than four new words are introduced on any page.

A more detailed explanation of the vocabulary count is given in the Manual that accompanies *Roads to Everywhere.*

## New Words in This Book

**UNIT I**

8 beyond
  *mysterious*\*
  *whom*
  meet
  *ill*
  moment
9 . . .

10 Benjie
11 Nellie
  fear
  delight
  reminder
12 lantern\*
13 steady
  throb\*
  smoothly
  flare
14 . . .
15 o'clock
16 led
  reins\*
17 slap
18 gallop
  shivered
  December
19 . . .
20 . . .
21 forget

22 explorer
  Rex

23 able
  wiggle
  foolish
24 . . .
25 dug
26 settled
  sight
  fairyland
27 footprints
28 person
29 rescued\*
30 knees
31 echo\*
  scolding
32 museum\*

33 Randy
  Melendy\*
  Oliphant\*
  Cuffy
34 burst
  grumbled\*
  Oliver
  Mona
35 practice
  beginner
  bike
36 . . .
37 trouble
  sloped\*
38 forehead\*
39 Wheelwright\*

40 bathtub
  wound\*
41 ago
  sofa\*
42 . . .
43 . . .
44 bruises
  scar
  hopefully

45 Becky
  bandit
  curls
46 instead
  daughter
  Simon's
  plan
47 San Joaquin\*
  mine
  tax
  paid
48 middle
  Murrieta\*
  steal
  cruel
49 . . .
50 spoke
  forward
  creek
51 . . .
52 . . .
53 reason
54 . . .

55 . . .
56 *señorita*\*
  *adiós*\*

57 Daniel
  Boone
  cabin
58 Rebecca\*
  marry
59 settlement\*
60 Kentucky\*
  battleground
  bloody
  wilderness\*
61 months
  fort
  attacked
  Boonesborough\*
62 Jemima\*
  dare
  fiercely\*
63 prisoners
64 hidden
65 braids
  famous\*
66 . . .
67 . . .

68 *jolly*
  pair
  sort
  *beef*
  *chest*

460

69 *Jimmy*
*whether*
*perhaps*
*iceberg*
*midnight*

70 true
list
kept
courage
71 encyclopedia
describing
match
skill
72 . . .

**UNIT II**

73 favorites

74 tailor
stroke
sewing
jam
75 slashing
dead
exclaimed
thread
76 clump
scornful*
77 killed
test
squeezed
soared*
78 huge*
crouched*
79 seized*
80 heels
excitement*
81 kingdom*
destroy*
belong
cottage
82 rough*
83 rage
unicorn*
84 least
85 chopped
boar
chapel

86 chisel*
carriage*
sunshade
wizard*

87 journey
beams*
power
88 . . .
89 . . .

90 Bruce
Scotland*
Robert
web*
91 fail
seventh
patiently*
flight

92 hung
*lacy*
*mist*
*strung*
*pearls*
*wove*
*pane*
*spun*
*single*
*jeweled*
motionless*
*kissed*

93 *nought**
*beetle*
*screech*
*cricket**

94 *tossed*

95 Icarus*
Daedalus*
angered
escape*
96 gulls
melted
wax
shaped
97 glorious*
wind-swept
glide
fluttering
98 freedom
human*
blazing
99 Sicily*
shepherds
gods
Apollo*
100 either
floated
notice

101 drowned
grief*
temple*
offering

102 Brahman*
fig
camel
jackal*
103 opinion*
judgment*
104 . . .
105 . . .
106 . . .
107 . . .
108 direction
109 . . .

110 report
sentence
display
library
111 share
unit
statements
characters
112 . . .

**UNIT III**

113 . . .
114 automobile
widow
Samuel
buggy
115 speed
rather
nuisance*
allowed
116 electrics
nonsense*
117 impossible
monstrosities*
modern
attention*
118 Hugo
goggles
Locomobile*
119 graze*
suggested
120 . . .
121 though

122 Kitty Hawk*
Orville*
Wilbur*
Wright*

123 level*
124 evening
weather
perfect
damaged*
125 successful
126 history
strap
waist
127 distance
128 gripping
handles
129 . . .
130 . . .
131 . . .

132 DeWitt*
Clinton*
133 England*
remained
coal
134 homely*
neigh*
crew
smokestack
135 Mathew
136 cheering
supply
137 hissed
excursion*
138 double
passengers
Schenectady*
139 y-ditty
rails
gleamed
forty-six
140 Albany*
141 nineteen
142 wrong

143 *store-ward*
*although*
*bold**
*obligingly*
*jay-walker*
*jeep*
squeal
*slam*
*jelly*

144 Merchandise*
Mart*
Chicago*
145 question
target

461

462

330 *Bing*
331 *Archbishop*
   *court*
   *pyjamas*
   *addressed*
   *note*
   *excuse*

332 mural
333 election
   candidates
   main
334 . . .

**UNIT VII**

335 . . .

336 Vic
   stables
337 nipped
   barrier*
338 snort
   buck
339 Arizona*
   George
   floods
340 . . .
341 . . .
342 . . .
343 hoofs
344 . . .
345 heroes

346 . . .
347 monument*
348 colonies*
   Utah*
   study
349 mineral*
350 . . .
351 since
   oranges
352 . . .
353 June
   parents
354 . . .
355 . . .

356 Hudson
   deck
357 yesterday
358 . . .
359 bay
   anchored*
360 . . .
361 . . .
362 . . .
363 . . .

364 chestnuts*
   balancing*
365 . . .
366 . . .

367 *Washington**
   *minnows*
   *hooted*
   *whippoorwills**
   *slender*
   *bugles*
   *summons**
   *rim*
   marched
   peace
   *strife**

368 Niagara*
369 reservation*
   ridge*
   bundle
   Joseph
370 harness
371 willows
   gorge*
372 migrating*
373 nickel*
374 . . .
375 yelled
376 choking
   struggling
377 . . .
378 . . .
379 . . .

380 responsibility*
   spelled
   contest
381 eighty
   whispering
   Dirk
   ma
382 debate*
   glare
383 silent
384 . . .
385 . . .
386 bushel
387 sigh
388 . . .
389 . . .
390 . . .

391 *nation's*
   *truth*
   *sake*
   *suffer*
   *pillars**

392 . . .
393 . . .
394 . . .

**UNIT VIII**

395 . . .

396 leaning
   bazaars
   floes*
   altogether
   wands
   vagabonds*

397 Abd el
   Karuzeh*
   flocks
   crags*
398 among
399 hyenas*
400 therefore
   ledge*
401 Feragi*
   Fuad*
   relief*
402 abandon*
   pity
403 *yah hya ris**
404 . . .
405 bleating
406 savage*
407 . . .
408 . . .
409 sank

410 Lars*
   Turi*
   Lapp*
   reindeer
411 Tomos*
   porridge*
   gasped
   lassoes*
412 skis
   speck
413 . . .
414 . . .
415 . . .
416 . . .
417 plain
418 . . .
419 . . .

420 . . .
421 . . .

422 *whither**
   *entangling*
   *oar*
   *dangling*
   *wary**
423 *lurks**
   *mermaid**
   *glistens**
   *prow**
   *flee*

424 Alec
   Evans
   Nanook*
   cache*
425 Sutherland
   coast
426 . . .
427 patrol*
   caribou*
   Fram*
428 . . .
429 . . .
430 Nick
431 Kootawuk*
   Port
   Radium*
432 depending
433 . . .
434 regular*
   routes*
435 kayaks*

436 Totaram*
   tease
437 Jai*
438 Wednesday
   pool
439 . . .
440 enormous*
441 . . .
442 . . .
443 . . .

444 . . .
445 . . .
446 . . .

D E F G H I J K L M N  0 6 9 8 7 6 5 4 3 2 1
PRINTED IN THE UNITED STATES OF AMERICA